CHM 2025L

Introduction to College Chemistry Lab

Florida SouthWestern State College

Signature Labs

CENGAGE
Learning·

Australia • Brazil • Japan • Korea • Mexico • Singapore • Spain • United Kingdom • United States

CENGAGE
Learning·

CHM 2025L
Introduction to College Chemistry Lab
Florida SouthWestern State College

Executive Editors:
 Maureen Staudt
 Michael Stranz

Senior Project Development Manager:
 Linda deStefano

Marketing Specialist:
 Courtney Sheldon

Senior Production/Manufacturing Manager:
 Donna M. Brown

Production Editorial Manager:
 Kim Fry

Sr. Rights Acquisition Account Manager:
 Todd Osborne

CHM 2025L, Intro to College Chemistry Lab
Signature Labs

© 2012, Thomson Corporation, a part of the Thomson Corporation.
Cengage Learning. All rights reserved.

For product information and technology assistance, contact us at
Cengage Learning Customer & Sales Support, 1-800-354-9706

For permission to use material from this text or product,
submit all requests online at **cengage.com/permissions**
Further permissions questions can be emailed to
permissionrequest@cengage.com

This book contains select works from existing Cengage Learning resources and was produced by Cengage Learning Custom Solutions for collegiate use. As such, those adopting and/or contributing to this work are responsible for editorial content accuracy, continuity and completeness.

Compilation © 2012 Cengage Learning
ISBN-13: 978-1-285-10063-0

ISBN-10: 1-285-10063-8

Cengage Learning
5191 Natorp Boulevard
Mason, Ohio 45040
USA
Cengage Learning is a leading provider of customized learning solutions with office locations around the globe, including Singapore, the United Kingdom, Australia, Mexico, Brazil, and Japan. Locate your local office at:
international.cengage.com/region.

Cengage Learning products are represented in Canada by Nelson Education, Ltd.
For your lifelong learning solutions, visit **www.cengage.com/custom.**
Visit our corporate website at **www.cengage.com.**

Printed at CLDPC, USA, 11-19

Acknowledgements

The content of this text has been adapted from the following product(s):

TECH0600: Practicing Safety in the Chemistry Laboratory
ISBN-10: (0-87540-600-9)
ISBN-13: (978-0-87540-600-8)

TECH0511: Laboratory Techniques: Measuring the Volume of Liquids
ISBN-10: (0-87540-511-8)
ISBN-13: (978-0-87540-511-7)

PROP0375: Separating the Components of a Ternary Mixture
ISBN-10: (0-87540-375-1)
ISBN-13: (978-0-87540-375-5)

STOI0497: Reacting Vinegar with Baking Soda
ISBN-10: (0-87540-497-9)
ISBN-13: (978-0-87540-497-4)

ANAL0619: Titrating the Acetic Acid in Vinegar
ISBN-10: (0-87540-619-X)
ISBN-13: (978-0-87540-619-0)

MISC0490: Using Exponential Notation and Significant Figures
ISBN-10: (0-87540-490-1)
ISBN-13: (978-0-87540-490-5)

MISC0521: Using Statistics to Analyze Experimental Data
ISBN-10: (0-53497-762-6)
ISBN-13: (978-0-53497-762-7)

PROP0383: Density of Liquids and Solids
ISBN-10: (0-87540-383-2)
ISBN-13: (978-0-87540-383-0)

ANAL0387: Percent Water in a Hydrate
ISBN-10: (0-87540-387-5)
ISBN-13: (978-0-87540-387-8)

REAC0389: Single Replacement Reactions and Relative Reactivity
ISBN-10: (0-87540-389-1)
ISBN-13: (978-0-87540-389-2)

MISC0408: Representing Data Graphically
ISBN-10: (0-87540-408-1)

ISBN-13: (978-0-87540-408-0)

MISC0486: Dimensional Analysis
ISBN-10: (0-87540-486-3)
ISBN-13: (978-0-87540-486-8)

MISC0629: Naming Inorganic Chemical Substances
ISBN-10: (0-53497-760-X)
ISBN-13: (978-0-53497-760-3)

Table Of Contents

Practicing Safety in the Chemistry Laboratory

Prepared by M. L. Gillette, Indiana University Kokomo,
H. A. Neidig, Lebanon Valley College,
and J. N. Spencer, Franklin and Marshall College

PURPOSE OF THE EXERCISE

Learn behaviors that promote safe laboratory experiences. Sign a safety agreement confirming your promise to follow safe practices in the laboratory.

BACKGROUND INFORMATION

Your awareness of potential hazards and your respectful approach to the work you are going to perform are both essential to your safety in the chemistry laboratory. In addition, each person's safety in the laboratory depends on the responsible behavior of everyone else present.

The frequency of laboratory accidents can be sharply reduced if everyone follows all of the safety precautions and directions given for each experiment. In general, remember these three basic rules:

- Read the entire experiment before coming to the laboratory.

- Follow established procedures when working with laboratory materials and apparatus.

- Know how to get help if an accident does occur.

Safe Laboratory Practices

1. **Wear departmentally approved safety goggles at all times.**

   Always wear departmentally approved safety goggles in the chemistry laboratory, regardless of any corrective eyewear you may require. Contact lenses may be worn in most laboratory environments, provided that approved safety goggles are also worn. However, contact lenses may not be worn in areas where you may be exposed to certain OSHA-regulated substances. Your laboratory instructor will advise you when contact lenses are not permitted.

2. **Know the exact location and operation of all safety equipment in the laboratory.**

   Your laboratory instructor will identify the locations and explain the procedures for using the eyewash fountain(s), safety shower(s), fire alarm, fire blanket(s), fire extinguisher(s), fire pail(s), material safety data sheets, and first aid station(s). Your laboratory instructor will also point out the telephone and the emergency exit nearest to your laboratory bench. Learn the locations and policies for uses of these items—your safety depends on them.

Complete the **Safety Information** section later in this module.

3. *Never* **work alone in the laboratory.**

A laboratory instructor will always be present during an assigned laboratory period. If you encounter **any** difficulties, the instructor will be available to assist you. *Never* begin or continue any laboratory work without an instructor being present.

4. **Do only the experiment assigned by your laboratory instructor.**

Never do unauthorized work in the laboratory. In addition, do not alter the designated experimental procedure without your instructor's permission.

5. **Wear protective clothing.**

To protect your feet and legs from spilled chemicals, broken glass, or falling apparatus, do not wear open-toed shoes or sandals, and make sure that your legs are covered. Do not wear clothing with loose sleeves. Your laboratory instructor may ask or require you to protect your clothing by wearing a nonflammable, nonporous laboratory apron or a laboratory coat. Tie back long hair so that it will not fall into flames or chemicals, or become caught in equipment or machinery.

6. **Keep the laboratory bench and floor around your work area uncluttered.**

Place such items as purses, bookbags, coats, and books in designated areas, not on the laboratory bench or on the floor around your work area. Place only authorized materials, such as laboratory instructions, a notebook, and a pen or pencils, on your laboratory bench.

7. *Never* **eat, drink, use tobacco, or apply lip balm in the laboratory.**

To avoid contact with toxic substances, either airborne or spilled on the laboratory bench, *never* bring food or cigarettes into the laboratory. *Never* drink from laboratory glassware, because it might be contaminated. Keep your hands away from your face and mouth.

8. **Come prepared, and use good judgment and care when working in the laboratory.**

Carefully read the entire experiment before you come to the laboratory. Make sure that you understand all cautions about potential hazards and all warnings concerning critical steps in the procedure. Report to the laboratory on time, so as not to miss any important instructions from your laboratory instructor.

Do not use cracked or chipped glassware. Replace it with undamaged glassware.

Never taste any chemical in the laboratory.

Avoid inhaling fumes of any kind. If you are directed to detect an odor in an experiment, gently waft the vapors toward your nose with a cupped hand, or use the method recommended by your laboratory instructor. *Never* put your face directly over a container, such as a test tube, and directly inhale vapors.

Inform your instructor of any allergies or medical conditions you have that might affect your performance in the laboratory.

9. **Read reagent bottle and container labels** *carefully.*

   Make certain that you are using the appropriate chemicals and solutions for the experiment. Before you transfer a chemical or solution from a reagent bottle, carefully read the label. Record the identity of the reagent and, if appropriate, its concentration on your Data and Observations sheet or in your laboratory notebook. To ensure accurate identification of the reagent, read the label again before you put the container back on the shelf.

   Be sure to note whether or not there is a National Fire Protection Association (NFPA) diamond-shaped hazard label on the reagent bottle. A typical NFPA label is shown in Figure 1. These labels list the NFPA hazard ratings for the substance in the bottle, including any personal protection required when using the reagent. The ratings run from 0 to 4, representing least to most hazardous, respectively.

   Never pour unused reagents back into the reagent bottle. Instead, dispose of leftover reagents as directed by your laboratory instructor.

   Material safety data sheets (MSDS) for all chemicals used in a laboratory must be on file at a location known to the laboratory instructor. Federal law requires that chemical suppliers make the MSDS information available to users of these chemicals. The first section of an MSDS usually lists all the names by which the chemical is known, its chemical formula, supplier's name, and, if applicable, the NFPA hazard ratings. The remaining sections may include such information as physical data, fire and explosion hazards, reactivity data, health hazards, spills and disposal procedures, special protection information, and storage and handling procedures. MSDS vary, from supplier to supplier, in terms of their exact layout and contents. Part of a typical MSDS for acetone is shown in Figure 2 on the next page.

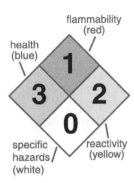

Figure 1
A typical NFPA hazard label

10. **Avoid burns from hot objects.**

    When you heat a chemical in a container, the burner (or hot plate) and the clamp holding the container also get hot. Do not touch hot objects. Do not place hot objects directly on the laboratory bench or a towel. Instead, use tongs to place hot objects on a heat-resistant mat or board.

11. **Use a fume hood when you are directed to do so.**

    Fume hoods safely remove toxic, irritating, and flammable vapors from the laboratory.

12. *Immediately* **report** *all* **injuries, no matter how minor, to your laboratory instructor.**

    Your laboratory instructor will help treat any injuries and keep a written record of all accidents that occur in the laboratory.

13. **Dispose of used materials according to your laboratory instructor's directions.**

    For the safety of the people who process discarded materials, dispose of all materials in properly marked containers.

MATERIAL SAFETY DATA SHEET

Section 1. IDENTITY

Name **ACETONE**
Synonyms **2-PROPANONE, DIMETHYLKETONE**
Formula **CH$_3$C(O)CH$_3$**
RTECS No. **AL3150000**
CAS No. **67-64-1**

NFPA Hazard Rating
health 1
flammability 3
reactivity 0

Section 2. HAZARDOUS COMPONENTS

Component	%	TLV
ACETONE	100	1000 ppm (2375 mg/m^3)

Section 3. PHYSICAL DATA

Clear, colorless, volatile liquid with a characteristic mint-like odor. Soluble in alcohol, ether, benzene, chloroform, most dimethylformamides, and oils.
Boiling point: 133 °F (56 °C). Specific Gravity: 0.7899
Volatility: 100% Vapor pressure: 180 mm Hg @ 20 °C

Section 4. FIRE, EXPLOSION HAZARDS

Dangerous fire hazard when exposed to heat or flame. Vapors are heavier than air and may travel a considerable distance to source of ignition.
Flash point: −4 °F (−20 °C).

Section 5. HEALTH HAZARDS

Inhalation: Irritant and narcotic. 20,000 ppm immediately dangerous to life.

Section 6. STORAGE AND HANDLING

Observe all Federal, state, and local regulations when storing or disposing of this substance. For assistance, contact the district director of the Environmental Protection Agency.
STORAGE: Store in accordance with 29 CFR 1910.106. Bonding and grounding: Substance with low electroconductivity that may be ignited by electrostatic sparks should be stored in containers that meet the bonding and grounding guidelines specified in NFPA 77-1983. Store away from incompatible substances.

Section 7. SPILLS AND DISPOSAL

Disposal must be in accordance with standards applicable to generators of hazardous waste; see 40 CFR 262. EPA hazardous waste number U002. Occupational spill: Shut off ignition sources. Stop leak if you can do so without risk. Use water spray to reduce vapors. For small spills, take up with sand or other absorbent material, and place into containers for later disposal.

Figure 2
A partial MSDS for acetone, showing a typical MSDS format

14. **Help keep the laboratory clean at all times.**

    Clean up any spilled chemicals in the area around the balances and on the laboratory bench. Before you leave the laboratory, wipe the bench top thoroughly, and properly dispose of burned matches and paper scraps.

15. **Wash your hands thoroughly before you leave the laboratory.**

    Before you leave the laboratory, wash your hands thoroughly with soap or detergent to remove all traces of reagents from your skin.

If an Accident Does Occur

In spite of the best efforts of all concerned, laboratory accidents do occur. Consequently, you must know what to do in response to particular situations.

The following examples illustrate some of the more common types of accidents that occur. Your laboratory instructor will elaborate on the general information presented here. In addition, your instructor may suggest modifications of these procedures that will make them more appropriate for your laboratory.

Burns

Immediately notify your laboratory instructor about any burn. Burns from hot objects, flames, or chemicals should all be treated in the same way: Flush the affected area with cool, running water for 20 minutes. Your instructor will determine whether or not the burn should receive medical attention.

Cuts and Wounds

Immediately notify your laboratory instructor about any cut or wound you receive in the laboratory. All such wounds should be considered serious and treated carefully. Your instructor will determine what kind of medical care is needed.

Chemical Spills on the Laboratory Bench, Reagent Shelf, or Floor

Immediately notify your bench neighbors and your laboratory instructor about any spill and the substances involved. Clean up the spill as directed by your laboratory instructor.

If the spill involves volatile, flammable materials, tell everyone in the laboratory to extinguish all flames. Disconnect any spark-producing equipment. Shut down all experiments. Evacuate the laboratory, if your laboratory instructor tells you to do so.

Chemical Spills on a Person

Over a Large Area. *Immediately* notify your laboratory instructor about any large spill on a person. Your instructor might take one or both of the following actions, depending on the extent and location of the spill:

Using the safety shower, flood the affected body area with cold water for at least 20 minutes. Quickly remove all contaminated clothing while the person is under the shower.

Wash off chemicals using a mild detergent solution. Rinse the affected area with cold water.

In either case, your laboratory instructor will obtain medical assistance immediately.

Over a Small Area. *Immediately* flush the area thoroughly with cold water. Notify your laboratory instructor, who will take any appropriate further action.

In the Eyes. *Immediately* call for assistance in getting to the nearest eyewash fountain. Drench your eyes for at least 20 minutes, carefully holding them wide open. Rotate your eyeballs in order to flush all areas. Meanwhile, your laboratory instructor will obtain the necessary medical assistance.

If a chemical splashes on your face while you are wearing safety goggles, *keep the goggles on*. If you remove the goggles immediately following such a spill, the splashed chemical may get into your eyes.

Instead, *immediately* get to the nearest eyewash fountain, and drench your face and goggles. When you have completely rinsed the chemical from your face and goggles, remove the goggles. Then proceed to drench your eyes for at least 20 minutes, as described above.

Ingesting Chemicals

Immediately notify your laboratory instructor if you accidentally ingest a chemical. Your instructor will take appropriate action for the specific substance ingested.

Unconsciousness

Inhalation of, or skin contact with, certain chemicals can cause respiratory failure, resulting in unconsciousness. Electric shock can have the same effect. If anyone becomes unconscious in the laboratory, *immediately* call for your laboratory instructor.

Fire

Immediately alert the proper authorities about any fire and its status. Call for additional assistance, if needed. In the case of a major fire, go to a safe area agreed upon by the emergency responders, and wait there to direct them to the fire.

If your clothing is burning, *immediately* move away from the source of the fire and *stop–drop–roll: Stop* what you are doing, *drop* to the floor, and *roll* over and over to extinguish the flames. *Call for help.* Keep rolling until someone else gets a fire blanket to help smother the flames on your clothing.

If your clothing is burning, *do not run* to the fire blanket or safety shower. Running fans the flames, increasing your chances of sustaining respiratory damage from inhalation of hot, toxic fumes.

If someone else's clothing catches fire, *immediately* move the person away from the source of the fire. Make them *stop–drop–roll*. Use the fire blanket to help smother the flames. *Immediately* call for your laboratory instructor. Remove the fire blanket as soon as the flames have been extinguished, so that the victim will not be burned further by hot clothing.

While the victim is being cared for, other people should try to shut off or at least reduce the fuel supply to the fire, unless your laboratory instructor has told you to evacuate the laboratory. If the fire is small, and you have experience in doing so and are confident of success, control and extinguish the fire by directing the spray of an appropriate fire extinguisher at the *base* of the fire.

Safety Information

The safety information presented here applies to any chemistry laboratory. Therefore, make yourself thoroughly familiar with it. Many experiments also contain additional warnings about steps or reagents that may be hazardous. For this reason, it is important that you read the entire experiment before you attempt to carry out the procedure.

Be especially aware of the safety resources in your laboratory. The safety equipment and related facilities usually found in a typical chemistry laboratory are listed below. Next to each item, record its location in your laboratory. There is also room to record important telephone numbers and additional safety instructions that your laboratory instructor may give you. In an emergency, this information will help you to quickly take the correct action. A few seconds saved can mean the difference between severe injury or damage and a minor inconvenience.

When you have finished recording all the safety information, ask your laboratory instructor to sign and date this page. Make sure you have this page with you whenever you are working in the laboratory.

Location of Safety Resources

eyewash fountain: nearest emergency exit:

safety shower: fire extinguisher:

first aid station: fire blanket:

material safety data sheets: nearest telephone:

fire alarm: fire pail:

Emergency Telephone Numbers

fire: poison center: police:

Additional Safety Instructions

_____   _____
student's signature   date

_____   _____
laboratory instructor's signature   date

Carefully read the following **Chemistry Laboratory Safety Agreement**. Once you have read and understood the Agreement, you must sign it. Then you must ask your laboratory instructor to sign it.

Chemistry Laboratory Safety Agreement

Any time I am working in, or even visiting, the laboratory, I will follow the laboratory safety practices recommended in this module, and I will take the following precautions:

1. Wear departmentally approved safety goggles at all times.
2. Know the exact location and operation of all safety equipment in the laboratory.
3. *Never* work alone in the laboratory.
4. Do only the experiment assigned by my laboratory instructor.
5. Wear protective clothing.
6. Keep the laboratory bench and floor around my work area uncluttered.
7. *Never* eat, drink, use tobacco, or apply lip balm in the laboratory.
8. Come prepared, and use good judgment and care when I work in the laboratory.
9. Read reagent bottle and container labels *carefully.*
10. Avoid burns from hot objects.
11. Use a fume hood when I am directed to do so.
12. *Immediately* report *all* injuries, no matter how minor, to my laboratory instructor.
13. Dispose of used materials according to my laboratory instructor's directions.
14. Help keep the laboratory clean at all times.
15. Wash my hands thoroughly before I leave the laboratory.

I have carefully read the discussion of recommended laboratory safety practices and the precautions listed above. I understand my role in protecting the safety of everyone in the laboratory. I agree to follow these practices and take these precautions whenever I am in the laboratory.

_____   _____
student's signature   *date*

_____   _____   _____   _____
course   *section*   *locker number*   *room number*

_____   _____
laboratory instructor's signature   *date*

_____   _____   _____
name   *section*   *date*

Laboratory Safety Quiz

1. Why is it important to tie back long hair when working in the laboratory?

2. Why should you never bring food into the laboratory?

3. What should you do if you spill a flammable liquid on your laboratory bench?

4. Why is it dangerous to wear open-toed shoes or sandals in the laboratory?

5. What procedure should you follow if a liquid splashes in your face while you are wearing safety goggles?

6. List the poor judgments and safety violations made by Thomas and his laboratory partner in the following scenario.

Thomas arrived a few minutes late for laboratory because he had been trying to find his syllabus, in order to determine which experiment he was scheduled to do. In his hurry, he had forgotten his safety goggles. He hoped his instructor would not notice. After unpacking his bookbag on the laboratory bench, Thomas discovered a half-eaten candy bar, which he put aside to finish later in the laboratory period. After Thomas and his partner started their experiment, they noticed a big crack in the beaker they were using. Because they were rushing to catch up with the rest of the class, they decided to continue with the experiment, which involved heating a solution in the beaker. The beaker broke, spilling a hot, corrosive solution on the laboratory bench. The solution ran onto the floor and Thomas's sandals, splashing his feet with hot, corrosive liquid. So as not to call attention to their problems, Thomas continued the experiment, using a different beaker, while his partner tossed the pieces of the broken beaker into a basket marked "paper only". That night, Thomas was unable to sleep because the burns on his feet, although superficial, were very painful.

Using Exponential Notation and Significant Figures

Prepared by Norman E. Griswold, Nebraska Wesleyan University

PURPOSE OF THE EXPERIMENT

Review exponential notation and use it to solve problems with and without a calculator. Review rules for determining significant figures and use them to round off calculations.

BACKGROUND INFORMATION

I. Exponential Notation

During your study of chemistry, you will encounter numbers ranging from the incredibly large to the extremely small. For example, a 100-mL sample of water contains more than 3 septillion molecules of water, or 3,000,000,000,000,000,000,000,000 molecules. Each water molecule has a mass of approximately 30 septillionths of a gram, or 0.000 000 000 000 000 000 000 03 grams. Representing very large or very small numbers this way is awkward and time consuming. Consequently, we usually use exponential notation, sometimes called **scientific notation**, to express such numbers.

A. Expressing Numbers Using Exponential Notation

Exponential notation expresses numbers as the product of two factors. The first factor, the **digit term**, is a number between 1 and 10. The digit term is multiplied by the second factor, called the **exponential term**, which has the form 10^x, 10 raised to a specific whole number power called the **exponent**.

For example, using exponential notation we represent 126 as 1.26×10^2, which we read as "one point two six times ten to the second". As shown in Figure 1, the digit term in this expression is 1.26. This term includes all the significant figures of the number being represented. (We will review the rules for determining significant figures in Part II of this module.)

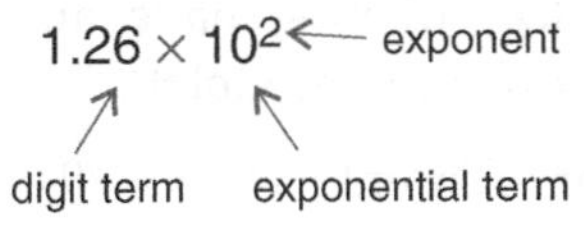

The exponential term in this example is 10^2. A positive exponent represents the number of times the digit term must be *multiplied* by 10 to give the number represented. For example, 1.26×10^2 means $1.26 \times 10 \times 10 = 126$.

$1.26 \times 10^2 \leftarrow$ exponent

digit term   exponential term

Figure 1
Exponential notation

Note that there are three figures in the digit term and three figures in the number being represented.

Some additional examples of numbers expressed in exponential notation are:

$$273.15 = 2.7315 \times 10^2$$
$$0.08206 = 8.206 \times 10^{-2}$$
$$0.001 = 1 \times 10^{-3}$$

These examples show that, when expressed using exponential notation, numbers greater than 10 have positive exponents and numbers less than 1 have negative exponents.

A negative exponent represents the number of times the digit term must be *divided* by 10 to give the number being represented. Thus, 2.46×10^{-3} means

$$2.46 \times \frac{1}{10} \times \frac{1}{10} \times \frac{1}{10} = 0.00246$$

Another way to interpret the exponent is to say that the exponent is equal to the number of places we must move the decimal point in a number to convert the number into the digit term. If the decimal point must be moved to the *left*, the exponent is positive. For example, the number 126 can be expressed as 1.26×10^2. The decimal point (following the 6 in 126) must be moved two places to the left to give the digit term, 1.26, so the exponent is a positive 2.

If the decimal point must be moved to the *right*, the exponent is negative. As another example, 0.00246 can be expressed as 2.46×10^{-3}. The exponential term is 10^{-3}, because the decimal point in 0.00246 must be moved three places to the right to give the digit term, 2.46. We could also express 0.00246 as 24.6×10^{-4}, 246×10^{-5}, or even as 0.246×10^{-2}. However, scientists usually keep the digit term between 1 and 10. For this example then, 2.46×10^{-3} is preferred, although the other expressions are acceptable.

B. Exponential Notation Using a Calculator

An electronic calculator is an important aid for performing chemical calculations. Your calculator may be slightly different from the one used for the following examples. If so, use your calculator's instruction book when performing these tasks.

To use exponential notation with your calculator, it must have an exponent key, usually labeled EXP (or EE or EEX on some models).

1. **Entering Exponential Numbers on a Calculator** To enter 1.26×10^2 on a calculator with an EXP key, press the following keys in the order shown.

$$\boxed{1}\ \boxed{\cdot}\ \boxed{2}\ \boxed{6}\ \boxed{EXP}\ \boxed{2}$$

To enter 2.46×10^{-3} on a calculator with an EXP key, press the following keys in order.

$$\boxed{2}\ \boxed{\cdot}\ \boxed{4}\ \boxed{6}\ \boxed{EXP}\ \boxed{+/-}\ \boxed{3}$$

The +/- key may be labeled CHS for "change sign".

Some calculators can be set so that the answers are automatically expressed in exponential notation on the display. If your calculator has the appropriate keys, select the exponential notation mode by pressing 2nd , then SCI . Other calculators require different keystrokes to select the exponential notation mode.

The following example shows the different answers obtained using the normal mode and the exponential notation mode.

normal mode : $(3.2 \times 10^{-3}) \times (5 \times 10^{-4}) = 0.0000016$

exponential notation mode : $(3.2 \times 10^{-3}) \times (5 \times 10^{-4}) = 1.6 \times 10^{-6}$

2. **Adding, Subtracting, Multiplying, and Dividing Exponential Expressions**   In order to use a calculator to add, subtract, multiply, or divide exponential expressions, we use the keys + , − , × or ÷ , which represent these operations, just as we would when manipulating numbers in normal notation. The only difference is that you must first select exponential notation mode. For example, use the following sequence of keystrokes to calculate $(3.2 \times 10^{-3}) \times (5 \times 10^{-4})$.

3 • 2 EXP +/− 3 × 5 EXP +/− 4 = $= 1.6 \times 10^{-6}$

3. **Determining Square Roots and Cube Roots of Exponential Expressions**   To obtain square roots of exponential numbers, remember that $\sqrt{A} = A^{1/2}$ and use the $\sqrt{x}$ or y^x key. For calculators with a y^x key, use the following sequence of keystrokes to find the square root of 2.7×10^{10}.

2 • 7 EXP 1 0 y^x • 5 = $= 1.6 \times 10^5$

The • and 5 keystrokes are used because $1/2 = 0.5$.

To obtain cube roots of exponential numbers, remember that $\sqrt[3]{A} = A^{1/3} = A^{0.333}$, and use the y^x key. For example, to take the cube root of 2.7×10^{10}, use the following sequence of keystrokes.

2 • 7 EXP 1 0 y^x • 3 3 3 = $= 2.97 \times 10^3$

4. **Taking Logarithms and Antilogs of Exponential Numbers**   A logarithm is an exponent: It is the power to which 10 must be raised in order to produce a given number. For example, $1.5 \times 10^4 = 10^{4.18}$. The given number is 1.5×10^4, and its logarithm is 4.18. The logarithm of 1.5×10^4, written as log 1.5×10^4, can be determined by the following sequence of keystrokes.

1 • 5 EXP 4 log $= 4.18$

The reverse of obtaining ("taking") a logarithm is taking the antilog. To take the antilog of 4.18, select the exponential notation mode on your calculator. Then use the following keystrokes to calculate antilog $10^{4.18}$.

1 0 y^x 4 • 1 8 = $= 1.5 \times 10^4$

If your calculator is not set for exponential notation mode, the answer will appear as 15135.612.

C. Using Exponential Numbers without a Calculator

1. **Adding and Subtracting Exponential Numbers** To add or subtract exponential numbers without a calculator, the numbers must have the same exponents. Consider the following example: $(1.27 \times 10^3) + (4 \times 10^1)$. One way to express these numbers so that they have identical exponents is to rewrite 4×10^1 as 0.04×10^3. Moving the decimal point two places to the left increases the exponent by two. The example then becomes $(1.27 \times 10^3) + (0.04 \times 10^3)$. Next, add the digit terms, the sum of which becomes the digit term of the answer. The final answer is the answer digit term multiplied by the common exponential term, as shown.

$$
\begin{array}{rcl}
1.27 \times 10^3 & \longrightarrow & 1.27 \times 10^3 \\
+\underline{4 \times 10^1} & \longrightarrow & +\underline{0.04 \times 10^3} \\
& & 1.31 \times 10^3
\end{array}
$$

The following is the result if we rewrite 1.27×10^3, rather than 4×10^1, before adding.

$$
\begin{array}{rcl}
1.27 \times 10^3 & \longrightarrow & 127 \times 10^1 \\
+\underline{4 \times 10^1} & \longrightarrow & +\underline{4 \times 10^1} \\
& & 131 \times 10^1 = 1.31 \times 10^3
\end{array}
$$

The answer is the same: It does not matter which number we change before addition. However, the first method directly gives the result in preferred exponential form (only one digit to the left of the decimal point).

The rules for subtraction of exponential numbers are the same as for addition, except that the digit terms are subtracted rather than added. Here are two examples:

$$
\begin{array}{rcl}
1.0 \times 10^2 & \longrightarrow & 10 \times 10^1 \\
-\underline{4 \times 10^1} & \longrightarrow & -\underline{4 \times 10^1} \\
& & 6 \times 10^1
\end{array}
$$

$$
\begin{array}{rcl}
3.2 \times 10^{-3} & \longrightarrow & 3.2 \times 10^{-3} \\
-\underline{5 \times 10^{-4}} & \longrightarrow & -\underline{0.5 \times 10^{-3}} \\
& & 2.7 \times 10^{-3}
\end{array}
$$

2. **Multiplying Exponential Numbers** When multiplying or dividing exponential numbers without a calculator, it is not necessary for the numbers to have identical exponents. To multiply exponential numbers, first multiply the digit terms. Then **add** the exponents to obtain the exponential term of the answer. A general expression for this procedure is:

$$(A \times 10^n)(B \times 10^m) = (A \times B) \times 10^{n+m}$$

Here are some specific examples:

$$(2 \times 10^4)(4 \times 10^2) = (2 \times 4) \times 10^{4+2} = 8 \times 10^6$$

$$(2 \times 10^4)(4 \times 10^{-2}) = (2 \times 4) \times 10^{4+(-2)} = 8 \times 10^2$$

$$(2 \times 10^{-4})(4 \times 10^{-2}) = (2 \times 4) \times 10^{(-4)+(-2)} = 8 \times 10^{-6}$$

Sometimes multiplying exponential numbers results in an answer in which the exponential term is 10^0. In such cases, remember that $10^0 = 1$ exactly; the exponential term can be dropped from the answer. For example:

$$(2 \times 10^4)(4 \times 10^{-4}) = (2 \times 4) \times 10^{4+(-4)} = 8 \times 10^0 = 8$$

3. **Dividing Exponential Numbers**   To divide exponential numbers, first divide the digit terms. Then *subtract* the exponent of the denominator from the exponent of the numerator to obtain the exponent of the answer. A general expression of this procedure is:

$$\frac{A \times 10^n}{B \times 10^m} = \frac{A}{B} \times 10^{n-m}$$

Some specific examples are:

$$\frac{6 \times 10^4}{3 \times 10^2} = \frac{6}{3} \times 10^{4-2} = 2 \times 10^2$$

$$\frac{6 \times 10^4}{3 \times 10^{-2}} = \frac{6}{3} \times 10^{4-(-2)} = 2 \times 10^6$$

$$\frac{6 \times 10^{-4}}{3 \times 10^{-2}} = \frac{6}{3} \times 10^{(-4)-(-2)} = 2 \times 10^{-2}$$

Name   Section   Date

Problem Set 1

(Use the spaces provided for the answers and additional paper if necessary.)

1. Some numbers of interest to chemists are given below. Express each number in proper exponential notation.

(a) 96,485 C (the Faraday constant)

(b) 299,792,458 m/s (speed of light in a vacuum)

(c) 0.0000000128 cm (radius of a metallic copper atom)

(d) 0.000001315 m (wavelength of an iodine laser)

2. Solve the following problems and express your answer in proper exponential notation. Try doing (a)–(d) without a calculator, first. Then do them with a calculator.

(a) $(3.8 \times 10^{-4}) + (4.000 \times 10^{-2}) =$

(b) $(2.40 \times 10^{6}) - (4 \times 10^{4}) =$

(c) $(2.10 \times 10^{8})(3.00 \times 10^{-14}) =$

(d) $\dfrac{7.69 \times 10^{6}}{2.00 \times 10^{-2}} =$

(e) $\left(\dfrac{2.73 \times 10^{-6}}{5.46 \times 10^{4}} \right) + (1.00 \times 10^{-3}) =$

(f) $\left(\dfrac{2.40 \times 10^{-6}}{1.20 \times 10^{4}} \right) + (3.48 \times 10^{-8}) =$

II. Significant Figures

One of the first concepts taught in chemistry is **density**, the mass of a substance divided by its volume. Suppose that, to help understand density, you are asked to determine the density of a metal sample as accurately as possible. Using an analytical balance, you determine the mass of the assigned metal sample as 14.3216 g. If its volume is 2.00 mL, what should you report as the density of the metal?

When more than 100 students were asked this question, they gave the following answers: 7.1608 (most common), 7.160, 7.161, 7.16, 7.1, 7.2, and "about 7." Are all these answers correct? If not, which is correct? Would these answers have differed if the mass had been reported as 14 g? How can you report experimental results in a way that indicates the exactness of the measurements involved? All these questions can be resolved by using some simple rules to determine the proper number of figures to use when reporting a result obtained from measurements. The proper number of figures to include are called **significant figures** or **significant numbers**.

The basic rule for determining significant figures is: **only those figures that are reasonably reliable are significant**. The following sections describe how to determine which figures in a measurement are reasonably reliable and, therefore, are significant figures.

A. Kinds of Experimental Values

Experimental values in chemistry consist of two broad groups: **exact numbers** and **inexact numbers**. The first group includes numbers that arise from counting or from certain definitions. For example, if we count the students in a chemistry class, we know the exact number of people in the class. Similarly, some numerical relationships are exact by definition. Such numbers can be thought of as having an infinite number of significant figures. Some examples include:

$$1.000 \text{ L} = 1000 \text{ mL}$$
$$1.000 \text{ cm} = 1.00 \times 10^7 \text{ nm}$$
$$1.00 \text{ g} = 1.00 \times 10^{-3} \text{ kg}$$

By definition, 1.000 liter is *exactly* equal to 1000 milliliters. These examples are all conversions within a given system of units, in this case, the metric system.

The second group, inexact numbers, consists of numbers resulting from measurements and approximate conversion factors. The exactness of a measurement depends upon the measuring device. For example, Figure 2 on the next page shows arrows positioned at identical locations on three scales that differ only in the number of measuring marks. In Figure 2(a), the estimated position of the arrow is 6 or 7. A more exact position cannot be obtained using the scale in Figure 2(a). Figure 2(b) shows that the arrow is slightly closer to 7 than to 6. Using the scale in Figure 2(b), we can estimate that the arrow is at 6.5 or 6.6. The scale in Figure 2(c) makes it clear that the arrow is closer to 6.6 than to 6.5. Using the scale in Figure 2(c), a reasonable estimate for the arrow position is about 6.58 or 6.59. As you can see, the exactness of a measurement depends on the measuring device.

Certain conversion factors are also inexact. This situation occurs when converting from one system of units to another system, such as converting

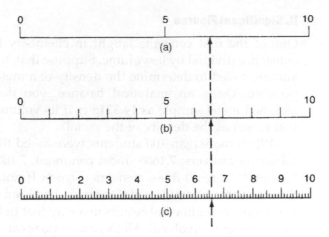

Figure 2
Examples of measurement using scales of varying precision

from the English system to the metric system. For example, by definition, the conversion of the mass unit called the English pound to the metric kilogram is:

$$1.00 \text{ lb} = 0.45359237 \text{ kg}$$

However, a more common (but less exact) conversion factor found in many tables is:

$$1 \text{ lb} = 0.4536 \text{ kg}$$

The number of significant figures in 0.45359237 and 0.4536 is different. Rules for determining the correct number of significant figures to use when reporting a measurement or calculation are given in the following section.

B. Determining the Number of Significant Figures

A reasonably reliable measurement contains at least one figure that is known with certainty, plus one estimated figure to the right of the last known figure. In Figure 2(b), for example, a reasonably reliable estimate of the arrow position is 6.6, although the arrow could be at either 6.5 or 6.7. In this case, the ones figure is known with certainty, and the tenths figure is estimated. Therefore, based on Figure 2(b), the number 6.6 contains two significant figures. If we were to report 6.62 as the arrow position for Figure 2(b), the second estimated figure, 2, would not be significant. In a reasonably reliable estimate, only one estimated figure can be included among the significant figures reported.

Similarly, for reported measurements or results, we assume that only the last numeral is estimated. Based on this assumption, it is not hard to determine the number of significant figures in reported values. For example,

1.75 has 3 significant figures
1.754 has 4 significant figures
17.54 has 4 significant figures

The following two rules apply to correctly reported values.

1. **All nonzero numerals are counted as significant figures**.

2. **The position of the decimal point has no effect on the number of significant figures, as long as the number contains no zeros**.

   For numbers containing zeros, common sense is very useful for determining the number of significant figures. For example, 2.016 clearly contains four significant figures: The zero is in the middle of the number, so it must be included. On the other hand, with small numbers like 0.08206 and large numbers like 135,000, there can be some confusion about whether zeros at the beginning or the end of a number should be counted. The following rules apply to counting zeros as significant figures.

3. **Zeros to the left of all nonzero numerals are not significant**.

   This means that you start counting significant figures at the nonzero numeral farthest to the left in the number, and count to the right. The following examples illustrate this rule:

   0.0821 contains 3 significant figures
   (start counting at the 8 and count to the right)
   0.002 has one significant figure
   (start counting at the 2)

4. **Zeros surrounded by nonzero numerals are significant**.
   The following examples illustrate this rule:

   200.59 has 5 significant figures

   2.016 has 4 significant figures

   0.08206 has 4 significant figures
   (start counting at the 8)

Note again that the position of the decimal point does not affect the number of significant figures.

5. **Zeros to the right of all nonzero numerals, called *trailing zeros*, may or may not be significant**.

   (a) **If a decimal point appears in the number, all trailing zeros to the right of the decimal point are significant.** For example:

   0.00640 has 3 significant figures (start counting at the 6;
   the last zero is to the right of all the nonzero digits and to
   the right of the decimal point; it is therefore significant)

   75.0 has 3 significant figures (same reasoning)

   1000.0 has 5 significant figures (all zeros are significant,
   because the last one is to the right of the decimal point)

   (b) **If trailing zeros are all to the left of the decimal point, then we must know more about the number to determine whether any of these zeros are significant.** Sometimes a reasonable guess is necessary. The following examples clarify this rule.

   The number 1000 may contain from one to four significant figures. For example, if you lift an object with your hand and guess that it weighs about 1000 g, this is obviously not an exact measurement.

In this case, the measurement and the number has only one significant figure, the 1. If you weigh the same object on a balance that determines mass to the nearest 10 g, then you can be reasonably certain of the first three figures in the measurement. In this case, 1000 has 3 significant figures. If you weigh the object on a balance that determines mass to the nearest gram, then all four figures in 1000 are significant.

As another example, the number 135,000 oz probably represents an approximate measurement, so it likely has only 3 significant figures. The zeros probably are there only to show the position of the decimal point. In cases like this, we cannot be sure whether any of the zeros are significant until we know something about the method of the measurement.

If we know the number of significant figures in 135,000 oz, we can indicate this clearly by using exponential notation to report the measurement number. This is because the digit term in exponential notation contains only significant figures. For example, if we know that a measurement of 135,000 oz has only one significant figure, we can show this clearly by expressing the number as 1×10^5 oz. If a much more exact measurement is made so that 135,000 oz has four significant figures, then we can express the measurement as 1.350×10^5. Thus, an important use of exponential notation is to clearly indicate the number of significant figures in a reported measurement.

C. Rounding Off Numbers

The next few sections explain how significant figures are used in calculations. The general rule about rounding is that **a calculated result can only be as reliable as the least precisely known measure ment in the calculation**. This rule makes it necessary to **round off** some numbers, that is, to drop certain digits.

Conventions for rounding off numbers focus on the digit farthest to the right of those that will be kept, the **retained digit**, and the next digit to the right, the **dropped digit**. Thus, if we round off 1.743 to 1.7, the retained digit is 7, and the dropped digit is 4. The following examples show numbers being rounded off to three significant figures.

1. **If the dropped digit is less than 5, the retained digit remains unchanged**.

   For example:

   1.634 rounds off to 1.63
   (4 is less than 5, so the 3 remains unchanged)
   1.6729 rounds off to 1.67
   (2 is less than 5, so the 7 remains unchanged)

2. **If the dropped digit is a 5 followed by zeros or no digits, the retained digit remains unchanged if it is an even number and is increased by one if it is odd**.

   For example:

   1.635 rounds off to 1.64
   (5 with no following digits is dropped,
   3 is odd, so the 3 is increased by 1 to 4)

1.625 rounds off to 1.62
(5 with no following digits is dropped,
2 is even, so the 2 remains unchanged)

1.07500 rounds off to 1.08
(5 followed by zeros is dropped,
7 is odd, so the 7 is increased to 8)

3. If the dropped digit is greater than 5 or is a 5 followed by nonzero digits, the retained digit is increased by 1.
For example:

1.637 rounds off to 1.64 (7 is greater than 5, so 3 is increased to 4)

1.647 rounds off to 1.65 (7 is greater than 5, so 4 is increased to 5)

1.48533 rounds off to 1.49 (5 is followed by nonzero digits,
so 8 is increased to 9)

D. Rounding off Calculated Results

In Part C, we noted that a calculated result is only as reliable as the least precisely known measurement in the calculation. We use this rule to determine how many digits to drop when rounding off a calculated result. The type of calculation determines how the rule is applied.

1. Rounding Off in Addition and Subtraction
In addition and subtraction, the least precisely known factor will be the one with the smallest number of decimal places. Therefore, the calculated result must have no more decimal places than the least precisely known number being added or subtracted.

For example, suppose a solution contains 99.6 g of A, 31.62 g of B, and 9.765 g of C. What should be reported as the total mass of the solution? We solve this problem as follows:

mass of A:	99.6 g	$\rightarrow$	99.6 g
mass of B:	31.62 g	$\rightarrow$	31.6 g
mass of C:	9.765 g	$\rightarrow$	9.8 g
total mass:			141.0 g

In other words, we round off all factors until there are no blank spaces in the right-hand column. When using a calculator to do the above addition, we either round off before adding (which requires fewer keystrokes) or we round off the result. In this case, if we use a calculator to add the original numbers, the result is 140.985. We then round off this number to 141.0, which matches the result we obtain when we round off the numbers before adding.

Rounding off in subtraction is done in the same way as in addition. For example, suppose that a beaker containing a solution weighs 72.654 g, while the empty beaker has a mass of 59.6 g. What is the mass of the solution?

mass of beaker and solution:	72.654 g	$\rightarrow$	72.7 g
mass of beaker:	59.6 g	$\rightarrow$	59.6 g
mass of solution:			13.1 g

Again, if we use a calculator, we must either round off the result or round off the factors first, as shown.

2. Rounding Off in Multiplication and Division

In multiplication and division, the result can be no more reliable than the least precisely known factor. The least precisely known factor in a multiplication or division problem calculation is simply the factor with the fewest significant figures, regardless of the position of the decimal point. The calculated result must be rounded off so that it contains no more significant figures than does the least precisely known factor.

For example, if we use a calculator to multiply 3.142 times 2.2 we get 6.9124. However, we should not report 6.9124 as our result, because the factor 2.2 contains only two significant figures. Therefore, the reported result can have only two significant figures, so 6.9124 must be rounded off to 6.9.

We can do some rounding off before multiplying or dividing. This will decrease the number of keystrokes needed. First, find the factor with the fewest significant figures. Round off all other factors so they have *one more* significant figure than the least precise factor. The calculated result will be the same as if you used the original factors and then rounded off the result at the end.

For example, consider the density calculation discussed at the beginning of this part of the Procedure:

$$d = \frac{14.3216 \text{ g}}{2.00 \text{ mL}} \begin{array}{l} \longleftarrow \text{(6 significant figures)} \\ \longleftarrow \text{(3 significant figures)} \end{array}$$

Using a calculator, we get the result 7.1608 g/mL, which must be rounded off to 7.16 g/mL (3 significant figures). The reported results, 7.16 g/mL, has the same number of significant figures as does the least precisely known factor, 2.00 mL.

To save keystrokes, we can round off the factors before dividing. In this case, we can round off 14.3216 g to four significant figures (14.32 g), *one more than* the three significant figures in 2.00 mL. Then we can divide as follows:

$$\frac{14.32 \text{ g}}{2.00 \text{ mL}} = 7.16 \text{ g/mL}$$

Both methods yield the same result.

E. Significant Figures in Logarithms

Several areas of chemistry use logarithms, which have two parts, the characteristic and the mantissa. The **characteristic** consists of the digits to the left of the decimal point. The **mantissa** consists of the digits to the right of the decimal point. For example, log 2578 = 3.4113. In the logarithm 3.4113, the characteristic is 3 and the mantissa is 4113.

One basic rule governs the number of significant figures that should be reported in a logarithm: **the mantissa of a logarithm should have the same**

number of significant figures as does the original number. Some examples are:

$$\log 2 = 0.3 \text{ (1 significant figure in 2)}$$
$$\log 2.0 = 0.30 \text{ (2 significant figures in 2.0)}$$
$$\log 2.00 = 0.301 \text{ (3 significant figures in 2.00)}$$
$$\log 2.0 \times 10^4 = 4.30 \text{ (2 significant figures in 2.0)}$$
$$\log 2.00 \times 10^{-5} = -4.699 \text{(3 significant figures in 2.00)}$$

The rule also applies when determining antilogs. Some examples:

$$\text{antilog } 0.48 = 3.0$$
$$\text{(2 significant figures in the mantissa)}$$

$$\text{antilog } 0.477 = 3.00$$
$$\text{(3 significant figures in the mantissa)}$$

$$\text{antilog } 3.4771 = 3.000 \times 10^3$$
$$\text{(4 significant figures in the mantissa)}$$

_____   _____   _____
Name   *Section*   *Date*

Problem Set 2

(Use the spaces provided for the answers and additional paper if necessary.)

1. How many significant figures are contained in each of the following numbers?

    (a) 0.9463   _____

    (b) 0.08206   _____

    (c) 6.0225×10^{23} _____

    (d) 1.0×10^{-12} _____

    (e) 1010   _____

2. Round off each of the following numbers to four significant figures.

    (a) 273.15   _____

    (b) 12.652   _____

    (c) 19.9743   _____

    (d) 4.32156   _____

    (e) 0.019807   _____

3. Complete the following calculations, and express each result using the proper number of significant figures.

   (a) $4.196 + 0.0725 + 14.3 =$

   (b) $74.321 - 4.2 =$

   (c) $(8.2156 \times 10^2) \times (3.12) =$

   (d) $\dfrac{6.042}{7} =$

   (e) $\dfrac{0.98 \times 0.230}{0.08206 \times 298} =$

Dimensional Analysis

Prepared by S. Kay Gunter, Scottsdale, AZ, and
James P. Birk, Arizona State University

PURPOSE OF THE EXPERIMENT

Practice using dimensional analysis to solve general chemistry problems using clues such as units or dimensions associated with measurements.

BACKGROUND INFORMATION

How Do You Solve a Problem?

Beginning students in chemistry often see problem-solving as their greatest challenge. Many students believe that solving chemistry problems involves memorizing endless mathematical equations and formulas, a different one for every situation. Relax! Just as there are techniques you can practice to improve your golf game, guitar playing, or cooking, there are techniques that will improve your chemistry problem-solving skills.

One of the most helpful techniques for solving problems is **dimensional analysis**. "Dimensional" refers to the dimensions, or units, associated with the numbers in the problem, such as 60 *seconds/minute* or 120 *grams/liter*. Dimensional analysis is based on the principle that the units in an equation can be treated like the numbers. In other words, in dimensional analysis, we perform the same mathematical operations on the units as we do on the associated numbers—division, multiplication, and especially cancellation.

To demonstrate how dimensional analysis works, let's analyze a problem we can solve almost without thinking. We'll break the problem-solving process into steps, write out the steps, and then apply the steps to solve more complicated everyday problems, as well as chemistry problems.

Here's the problem: Express 90 minutes in hours. For most of us, the answer comes automatically: 90 minutes is an hour and a half. Let's analyze the unconscious process we use to arrive at that answer. It takes a lot longer to explain it than to do it!

First, we decide what the problem asks us to find or calculate. In this case, it's straightforward: We need to find the number of hours (hr) that corresponds to 90 minutes (min).

To solve this problem, we have to know how many minutes there are in one hour. We can express this relationship as an **equivalence statement**: 1 hr = 60 min. From this equivalence statement, we can construct a **conversion factor** to change minutes into hours. To do so, we divide each side of the equivalence statement by 60 min:

$$\frac{1\,hr}{60\,min} = \frac{\cancel{60\,min}}{\cancel{60\,min}} = 1$$

Because we are dividing both sides by the same quantity, we know that the two sides of the resulting equation are also equal. Notice that the conversion factor, 1 hr/60 min, is equal to 1, an equivalence often called **unity**. This is true of all conversion factors, because the numerator and denominator always contain equivalent quantities. Because all conversion factors equal 1, we can multiply any measurement by a conversion factor without changing the total value of the measurement. All we are doing is changing the units used to express the measurement.

Next, we multiply the original quantity, 90 minutes, by the conversion factor to obtain the desired equivalent quantity expressed in hours:

$$90\,min \left(\frac{1\,hr}{60\,min}\right) = \frac{(90\,\cancel{min})(1\,hr)}{60\,\cancel{min}} = 1.5\,hr$$

Notice that the original unit, minutes, cancels, and the resulting quantity is expressed in the desired unit, hours.

Finally, we check the answer for reasonableness. We know that 90 min is longer than 1 hr, but not as long as 2 hr, so 1.5 hr is a reasonable answer.

To further study our reasonableness check, let's more closely examine our choice of conversion factor. For example, we can obtain another conversion factor from our original equivalence statement, 1 hr = 60 min, by dividing each side by 1 hr instead of 60 min.

$$\frac{1\,hr}{1\,hr} = \frac{60\,min}{1\,hr} = 1$$

This conversion factor is also equal to unity. However, look what happens when we multiply our original quantity, 90 min, by this conversion factor:

$$90\,min \left(\frac{60\,min}{1\,hr}\right) = \frac{(90\,min)(60\,min)}{1\,hr}$$

$$= 5400\,\frac{min^2}{hr}$$

There are two clear reasons why this answer is unreasonable: (1) the units (min²/hr) are definitely not the ones we want (hr); and (2) we know that 90 min isn't more than 5000 hr. Thus, we can conclude that 60 min/hr is the wrong conversion factor to use in solving this problem.

Every equivalence statement provides two such inverse conversion factors. The correct conversion factor to use depends on how the problem is expressed. In every case, when we use the correct conversion factor, the units we want to eliminate cancel, leaving only the units we want the answer expressed in. Using the incorrect conversion factor will give an unreasonable answer, expressed in nonsensical units. This should be a clear warning that we used an upside-down or otherwise incorrect conversion factor.

The preceding example illustrates the most compelling reason for using dimensional analysis to solve problems: it keeps us from multiplying when we should divide, or dividing when we should multiply. If the units in our answer are the desired ones, odds are good that we solved the problem correctly, barring arithmetic errors. If the units in our answer are not the desired ones, we probably used the wrong conversion factor. In problem solving, choosing incorrect conversion factors is more common than making arithmetic mistakes.

Now that we've analyzed a technique for solving an everyday problem, let's write out the steps and expand them, so the technique can be used to solve other types of problems, including chemistry examples:

Step 1.   Decide what the problem is asking you to do. Begin by reading the problem carefully. If the definitions of any terms are unclear, look them up. If an equation is given to use, be sure that you understand the meaning of any symbols or variables involved. Look for clues in the statement of the problem, words such as "calculate," "determine," "how much," "what mass," or "what volume." Once you understand what the problem is asking you to do, write down the units you will need for the answer.

Step 2.   Determine the relationships between the information given in the problem andthe desired answer. In our original example, we recognized that the relationship between the data given, "90 minutes," and the desired answer, "hours," could be expressed by the equivalence statement 1 hr = 60 min. This relationship was not stated in the original problem. We had to remember the relationship (or look it up), in order to apply it to this problem. When solving problems, you will often find that memory will serve as the source of these relationships. At other times you may need to refer to a previous paragraph, table, or figure in your textbook, a laboratory manual, or a data handbook.

As a word of caution, sometimes a problem contains more information than you need to solve it. Therefore, you should not assume that you must use a particular unit in your problem-solving calculations, just because the unit is included in the description of the problem. Critically examine all data and reject any data that aren't pertinent to the desired answer.

The equivalence statements must be valid. If we base our solution on an incorrect equivalence statement, such as 16 in. = 1 ft, or an unbalanced chemical equation, even dimensional analysis cannot help us to obtain the correct answer. However, as long as all the equivalence statements and equations we use are valid, dimensional analysis should keep us from making errors in either algebra or logic.

In our original example, the relationship between the two units could be expressed simply, as 1 hr = 60 min. However, the relationship is often more complex, requiring a series of related equivalence statements and their derived conversion factors. In other cases, a description of the relationship requires the use of an empirical or theoretical equation, or the application of a chemical principle. The section entitled "Applying Dimensional Analysis to General Chemistry Problems" on the next page presents examples of these and other problems.

Step 3.   Set up the problem by writing a logical, concise equation for solving the problem, based on the relationships determined in Step 2. Derive the conversion factors needed to achieve the desired answer. Be sure that the units you need to eliminate cancel, leaving only the desired units in the answer.

When a series of related conversion factors is required, map out the correct sequence to follow. For example, suppose that the solution to a problem involves the number of centimeters in one mile, but you can't find a table containing this information. However, you probably know (or can easily look up) the number of feet in one mile, the number of inches in one foot, and the number of centimeters in one inch. In this case, the correct sequence of units is:

$$\text{mi} \rightarrow \text{ft} \rightarrow \text{in.} \rightarrow \text{cm}$$

The equation needed to solve this problem should start with the quantity given, 1 mile, and then follow the above sequence, as shown in Equation 1.

$$1\,\text{mi} \left(\frac{5280\,\text{ft}}{1\,\text{mi}}\right)\left(\frac{12\,\text{in.}}{1\,\text{ft}}\right)\left(\frac{2.54\,\text{cm}}{1\,\text{in.}}\right) = 1.61 \times 10^5 \text{ cm} \qquad \text{(Eq. 1)}$$

Step 4. Check your answer to make sure it is reasonable in terms of both magnitude and units. This step is just as important as the preceding three. For example, suppose we are asked to calculate the daily volume of liquid antacid an ulcer patient must consume to neutralize his excess stomach acid. We calculate 24 L as the answer. Remembering that a liter and a quart are about the same volume, we realize that 24 L is an incredible amount of liquid for one person to drink daily. However, because liter is an acceptable volume unit for the answer, the conversion factors we used are probably correct. Therefore, we probably made an arithmetic error or omitted the metric prefix, milli- (10^{-3}), somewhere. Clearly, we need to recheck our calculations and, possibly, the equation we used for finding the answer, in order to find the error. If our answer had instead been 24 mol, we would know to check the conversion factors, because mole is not a volume unit.

When dealing with unfamiliar units or relationships, you may not always know whether or not an answer is reasonable. In such cases, just check your arithmetic.

SOLVING SAMPLE PROBLEMS IN DETAIL

We will work two problems in detail, analyzing the solutions step by step.

Example 1: Dimensional analysis may be applied to a relatively complicated non-chemical problem.

Problem: Calculate how many gallons of water are required to fill a residential fish pond, measuring 8.0 ft by 6.0 ft by 1.5 ft.

Step 1. The problem clearly states the physical dimensions involved and units desired in the answer: volume of water in gallons.

Step 2. The problem data are given in units of length (feet), but the answer must be in units of volume (gallons). Thus, we recognize that the first step is to calculate the volume of the pool:

$$\text{volume, ft}^3 = (l)(w)(h) = (8.0 \text{ ft})(6.0 \text{ ft})(1.5 \text{ ft}) = 72 \text{ ft}^3$$

Next, we need to know the relationship between cubic feet and gallons. A handbook tells us that 1 ft^3 = 7.481 gal (U.S.). Thus, the conversion is a simple one, described by the following equation.

$$72 \text{ ft}^3 \left(\frac{7.481 \text{ gal}}{1 \text{ ft}^3} \right) = 540 \text{ gal}$$

Step 3. If a data handbook is not available, we can solve this problem using the following simple equivalence statements that we either already know or can look up in a textbook:

1 ft = 12 in.	1 in. = 2.54 cm	10^3 cm^3 = 1 L
1 L = 1.06 qt	4 qt = 1 gal	

Our route for using the simple equivalency statements is:

$$\text{ft}^3 \rightarrow \text{in.}^3 \rightarrow \text{cm}^3 \rightarrow \text{L} \rightarrow \text{qt} \rightarrow \text{gal}$$

The correct equation is shown in Equation 2. Notice that if we raise to some power one of the units in a problem-solving equation (ft^3, for example), we must also raise to the same power all terms that contain that unit in the conversion factors. That's why the cm/in, factor is shown cubed. Otherwise, the units will not cancel. Also, notice that the answer is the same, when using the proper number of significant figures (two), regardless of the order of the conversion factors.

$$\text{volume, gal} =$$

$$72 \text{ ft}^3 \left(\frac{12 \text{ in.}}{1 \text{ ft}} \right)^3 \left(\frac{2.54 \text{ cm}}{1 \text{ in.}} \right)^3 \left(\frac{\text{L}}{10^3 \text{ cm}^3} \right) \left(\frac{1.06 \text{ qt}}{\text{L}} \right) \left(\frac{1 \text{ gal}}{4 \text{ qt}} \right)$$

$$= \frac{(72)(12)^3 (2.54)^3 (1)(1.06)(1 \text{ gal})}{(1)^3 (1)^3 (10^3)(1)(4)} = 540 \text{ gal} \qquad \text{(Eq. 2)}$$

Step 4. Because the units that cancel leave us with the units we want in our answer, we can feel confident that we used the correct conversion factors. If you don't know whether or not 540 gal is a reasonable estimate of the amount of water needed to fill a pond this size, check the arithmetic.

Example 2: Dimensional analysis can also be used within an equation.

Problem: Calculate the wavelength, in meters, of the radio waves broadcast from station KZON-FM, Phoenix, Arizona, operating at 101.5 MHz.

Step 1. The physical quantity and units desired are clearly stated: wavelength in meters.

Step 2. Hz is the symbol for hertz, a unit of frequency (1 Hz = 1 s^{-1}). Frequency and wavelength are related by the equation $\lambda v = c$, where λ = wavelength, v = frequency, and c = the speed of light in a vacuum, 3.00×10^{10} cm s^{-1}.

Step 3. The relationship $\lambda v = c$ may be rearranged to isolate wavelength: $\lambda = c/v$. Substituting the actual values for c and v, we obtain:

$$\lambda = \frac{3.00 \times 10^{10} \text{ cm s}^{-1}}{101.5 \text{ MHz}}$$

However, with the equation in this form, no units cancel. If we tried to use the equation to calculate λ, the answer would not be in meters. Instead, we must make some unit conversions within the equation. Knowing that $1 \text{ MHz} = 10^6 \text{ Hz}$ and $1 \text{ m} = 100 \text{ cm}$, we can convert $\text{MHz} \rightarrow \text{s}^{-1}$ and $\text{cm} \rightarrow \text{m}$. Then the units will cancel properly, leaving only meters in the answer:

$$\lambda, m = \left(\frac{3.00 \times 10^{10} \text{ cm s}^{-1}}{101.5 \text{ MHz}} \right) \left(\frac{1 \text{ MHz}}{10^6 \text{ Hz}} \right) \left(\frac{1 \text{ Hz}}{1 \text{ s}^{-1}} \right) \left(\frac{1 \text{ m}}{100 \text{ cm}} \right)$$
$$= 2.96 \text{ m}$$

Step 4. Because the units cancel properly, we can assume that the conversion factors are correct. Radio waves are among the longest electromagnetic waves, so this is not an unreasonable answer.

APPLYING DIMENSIONAL ANALYSIS TO GENERAL CHEMISTRY PROBLEMS

The following examples illustrate the use of dimensional analysis in solving general chemistry problems. Solving these problems will sharpen your problem-solving skills. Some problems use units that may not be familiar to you. Use dimensional analysis to solve these problems, even if you don't fully understand the meaning of the units involved. The meanings of such units and the bases for the equivalencies among them will become clearer to you as you proceed further in your study of chemistry.

In each of the following examples, Steps 1 and 4, deciding what the problem is asking for and checking the answer for reasonableness, respectively, are not written out. We only show Steps 2 and 3, which involve equivalence statements, sequences, and conversion factors. Use the metric prefixes and common equivalence statements in Tables 1 and 2 to solve these sample problems.

I. Simple Unit Conversions and Ratios of Units

Example 1: International soccer games are generally played on a field 115 yd long. Convert this distance to meters.

Answer 1: From Table 2, we know that $1 \text{ yd} = 0.9144 \text{ m}$, so the conversion equation is:

$$\text{distance, m} = 115 \text{ yd} \left(\frac{0.9144 \text{ m}}{1 \text{ yd}} \right) = 105 \text{ m}$$

Answer 2: If a table of equivalence statements were not available, you could calculate the distance using common equivalence statements that you probably already know, following the route:

Table 1 *Metric prefixes*

power of 10	prefix	symbol
−18	atto-	a
−15	femto	f
−12	pico	p
−9	nano-	n
−6	micro-	μ
−3	milli	m
−2	centi	c
−1	deci	d
+18	exa	E
+15	peta	P
+12	tera-	T
+9	giga	G
+6	mega-	M
+3	kilo-	k
+2	hecto-	h
+1	deka-	da

$$yd \rightarrow in. \rightarrow cm \rightarrow m$$

$$\text{distance, m} = 115 \, yd \left(\frac{36 \, in.}{1 \, yd}\right)\left(\frac{2.54 \, cm}{1 \, in.}\right)\left(\frac{1 \, m}{100 \, cm}\right)$$

$$= 105 \, m$$

Example 2: In our body-conscious culture, there's a lot of talk about the "calories" in various kinds of food. Few people remember that the original term was "Calorie," with a capital C, which actually means kilocalories (kcal).

To maintain their weight, moderately active people need to eat about 13,000 calories daily, or 13 Calories (kcal), per pound (lb) of body weight. Convert this amount of energy to kilojoules (kJ), another unit of energy.

Answer: Using Table 2, we find that a direct conversion is possible.

$$\text{energy, kJ} = 13,000 \, cal\left(\frac{4.184 \, J}{1 \, cal}\right)\left(\frac{1 \, kJ}{10^3 \, J}\right) = 54 \, kJ$$

Example 3: Calculate the total weight in pounds of a runner if his body weighs 158.0 lb, his clothes weigh 8.0 oz, and his shoes weigh 10.0 oz.

Answer: To add or subtract measurements, all units involved must be identical.

$$mass_{total} = mass_{runner} + mass_{clothes} + mass_{shoes}$$

Table 2 *Common equivalence statements*

mass:	1 lb = 0.4536 kg
	16 oz = 1 lb
	1 ton = 2000 lb
	1 amu = 1.6606×10^{-24} g
length:	1 in. = 2.54×10^{-2} m = 2.54 cm
	1 Å = 10^{-10} m = 10^{-8} cm
	1 ft = 12 in. = 0.3048 m
	1 yd = 3 ft = 36 in. = 0.9144 m
	1 mi = 1760 yd = 5280 ft
	$\quad$ = 1609 m
volume:	1 L = 10^{-3}m^3 = 1 dm^3 = 10^3 cm^3
	1 L = 1.06 qt
	1 gal = 4 qt = 8 pt = 3.785 L
	1 pt = 2 cups
	$\quad$ = 16 fluid ounces (fl oz)
time:	1 min = 60 s
	1 hr = 60 min = 3600 s
	1 d = 24 hr = 1440 min
	$\quad$ = 86,400 s
temperature:	°C = K − 273.15
	°C = 5/9(°F − 32)
force:	1 dyn = 10^{-5} N
pressure:	1 bar = 10^5 N/m^2 = 10^5 Pa
	1 torr = 1 mm Hg = 133.322 Pa
	1 atm = 760 torr = 101,325 N/m^2
	$\quad$ = 101,325 Pa
energy:	1cal = 4.184 J
	1 erg = 10^{-7} J
	1 eV = 1.6022×10^{-19} J

Based on Table 2, we can write either

$$\text{mass, oz} = 158.0\,\text{lb} \left(\frac{16\,\text{oz}}{1\,\text{lb}}\right) + 8.0\ \text{oz} + 10.0\ \text{oz}$$

$$= 2546\ \text{oz}$$

or

$$\text{mass, lb} = 158.0\ \text{lb} + (8.0\ \text{oz} + 10.0\ \text{oz})\left(\frac{1\,\text{lb}}{16\,\text{oz}}\right)$$

$$= 159.1\ \text{lb}$$

Example 4: Light in a vacuum travels at 3.00×10^{10} cm s^{-1}. Mars is an average of 141 million mi from Earth, and it travels in its orbit at 15 mi s^{-1}. How many hours would it take for a laser beam from the Earth to reach Mars?

NOTE: Two speeds are given in this problem, but only the speed at which light travels in a vacuum is relevant.

From Table 2 we know that 1 mi $= 1.609 \times 10^3$ m.

Answer: time = distance/speed

$$\text{time, hr} = \left(\frac{1.41 \times 10^8 \, \cancel{\text{mi}}}{3.00 \times 10^{10} \, \cancel{\text{cm s}^{-1}}} \right) \left(\frac{1.609 \times 10^3 \, \cancel{\text{m}}}{1 \, \cancel{\text{mi}}} \right)$$

$$\left(\frac{10^2 \, \cancel{\text{cm}}}{1 \, \cancel{\text{m}}} \right) \left(\frac{1 \, \text{hr}}{60 \, \cancel{\text{min}}} \right) \left(\frac{1 \, \cancel{\text{min}}}{60 \, \cancel{s}} \right) = .21 \, \text{hr}$$

NOTE: Using Tables 1 and 2, and the four basic steps for solving problems using dimensional analysis, solve the problems in Problem Set 1. Write your answers on a separate sheet of paper.

PROBLEM SET 1

1.1 On average, the moon takes 27 d, 7 hr, and 43.2 min to make a complete circuit around the Earth. Express this time in hours.

1.2 David Robinson, a professional basketball player, is 7 ft, 1.0 in. tall. Convert his height to centimeters.

1.3 A sheet of standard U.S. typing paper measures 8.50 in. $\times$ 11.0 in. What is its area in cm^2?

1.4 One of the oldest elephants on record lived for 130 yr. How many minutes is that? (Use 1 yr $=$ 365 d)

1.5 How many gallons of soft drink are there in a 2.0-L bottle?

1.6 What mass of cereal in kilograms is in a 40.0-oz box?

1.7 A diamond is made of pure carbon. The distance between any two neighboring carbon atoms in a diamond is 1.54 angstroms (Å). What is this distance in inches?

1.8 If an audiotape playing at a speed of 1.875 in. s^{-1} takes 45.0 min to play through one side, what is the length of the tape in feet? in meters?

1.9 The speed limit on many Australian highways is 100 km hr^{-1}. Convert this to mi hr^{-1} (round to the nearest whole number).

1.10 What is the volume in mL of 1.00 pt of heavy cream?

1.11 The average density of whole milk is 1.034 g cm^{-3}. What is its density in lb gal^{-1}?

1.12 It is 2374 mi between Phoenix, Arizona, and Philadelphia, Pennsylvania. What is this distance in km?

1.13 The legendary racehorse Secretariat won the 1973 Kentucky Derby with a time of 1 min, 59.4 s. The course is 1.25 mi long. Calculate the horse's average speed in mi hr^{-1}.

1.14 The density of water at room temperature (25 °C) is 0.9970 g cm^{-3}. How many pounds does the water in a full 5.00-gal pail weigh?

1.15 If the barometric pressure on a mountain top in Colorado is 521 mm of mercury, what is the pressure in inches of Hg? in atmospheres? in Pascals?

1.16 If an oxygen molecule is moving at 4.78×10^4 cm s^{-1}, what is its speed in mi hr^{-1}?

1.17 Nutrition experts recommend that you drink at least 8 cups of water daily. If your local water supply contains 1.00 part fluoride (by mass) per million parts water, how many milligrams of fluoride would you consume daily in your 8 cups of water? (Use 1.00 g cm^{-3} as the density of water.)

1.18 Light in a vacuum travels at a speed of 3.00×10^8 m s^{-1}. Pluto's average distance from the Sun is 3.6 billion miles. How many minutes does it take sunlight to reach Pluto?

1.19 The temperature of an oxyacetylene torch flame can reach as high as 3137 °C. What is this temperature in °F?

1.20 If the gasoline in a full 20.0-gallon tank weighs 116 lb, what is the density of gasoline in g mL^{-1}?

1.21 Dry sand has a density of 1.5 g cm^{-3}. A child's sandbox, measuring 4.0 ft by 5.0 ft, is filled with sand to a depth of 6.0 in. What is the mass of the sand in kg? in lb?

1.22 The hottest temperature yet recorded in Phoenix, Arizona, was 122 °F on June 26, 1990. What is that temperature in °C? in K?

II. Conversions among Masses, Moles, and Numbers of Particles

The relationships among mass, number of moles, and number of particles is shown by the following routes:

$$\text{mass} \xleftrightarrow{\text{AM, MM, or FM}} \begin{array}{c}\text{number}\\\text{of moles}\end{array} \xleftrightarrow{\text{N}} \begin{array}{c}\text{number of atoms,}\\\text{molecules, ions}\\\text{or forumula units}\end{array}$$

The double-headed arrows indicate that we can travel this route in either direction. We can also start at any point and travel only a portion of the entire route.

The symbols above the arrows indicate the data involved in the equivalence statements needed for making each conversion: atomic mass (AM), molar mass (MM), formula mass (FM), and Avogadro's number (N). These equivalence statements are determined as follows:

(a) 1 mol = amount of matter in 1 AM of *atoms:* 1 mol C = 12.01 g C

(b) 1 mol = amount of matter in 1 MM of *molecules:* 1 mol CO_2 = 44.01 g CO_2

(c) 1 mol = amount of matter in 1 FM of *formula units or ions*: 1 mol NaCl = 58.44 g NaCl; 1 mol SO_4^{2-} = 96.06 g SO_4^{2-}

(d) 1 mol = N = 6.022×10^{23} atoms, molecules, formula units, or ions: 1 mol CO_2 = 6.022×10^{23} CO_2 molecules; 1 mol NO_3^- = 6.022×10^{23} NO_3^- ions

Example 1: How many moles of NaCl are in 75.0 g of NaCl?

Answer: *mass of NaCl* $\xrightarrow{\text{FM}}$ number of molecules of NaCL

FM: 1 mol NaCl = 58.44 g NaCl

$$\text{number moles of NaCl, mol} = 75.0 \text{ g NaCl} \left(\frac{1 \text{ mol NaCl}}{58.44 \text{ g NaCl}} \right)$$

$$= 1.28 \text{ mol NaCl}$$

Example 2: How many molecules of CO_2 are in 25.0 g CO_2?

Answer: *mass* $\xleftrightarrow{\text{MM}}$ number of moles $\xleftrightarrow{\text{N}}$ number of molecules

MM: 1 mol CO_2 = 44.01 g CO_2

$$\text{number of molecules of } CO_2 = 25.0 \text{ g } CO_2 \left(\frac{1 \text{ mol } CO_2}{44.01 \text{ g } CO_2} \right)$$

$$\left(\frac{6.022 \times 10^{23} \text{ molecules } CO_2}{1 \text{ mol } CO_2} \right)$$

$$= 3.42 \times 10^{23} \text{ molecules } CO_2$$

PROBLEM SET 2

2.1 Find the number of moles in 100.0 g of each of the following:

(a) O_3 (ozone) (b) H_2SO_4 (sulfuric acid)
(c) $Ca_3(PO_4)_2$ (d) $C_{12}H_{22}O_{11}$ (table sugar)
(e) Au (gold)

2.2 Find the mass of 0.67 mol of each of the following:

(a) Ag (silver) (b) C_4H_{10} (butane)
(c) SiO_2 (quartz) (d) N_2O (laughing gas)
(e) $Mg(OH)_2$ (stomach antacid)

2.3 Find the number of particles in 100.0 g of each of the following:

(a) O^{2-} (b) O_2 (c) MgO
(d) $C_8H_{10}N_4O_2$ (caffeine) (e) $Fe_3Al_2(SiO_4)_3$ (garnet)

2.4 Find the mass of 2.00×10^{23} particles of each of the following:

(a) NH_3

(b) Na_2CrO_4

(c) $C_6H_{11}OBr$ (tear gas)

(d) $C_{10}H_{14}NO_5PS$ (parathion, an insecticide)

(e) $NH_2C_6H_4CO_2H$ (PABA, *para*-aminobenzoic acid)

III. Percent Composition and Chemical Formulas

The relationships connecting percent composition and chemical formulas are shown in the following route using a hypothetical compound composed of substances A and B.

$$\text{mass} \atop \% A \xleftarrow{\text{100-g sample}} \text{mass} \atop \text{of } A \xleftarrow{\text{AM}} \text{number of} \atop \text{moles of } A$$

$$\uparrow$$

$$\text{subscripts} \atop \text{in formula} \longleftrightarrow \text{empirical} \atop \text{formula} \xleftarrow{\text{MM and FM}} \text{molecular} \atop \text{formula}$$

$$\downarrow$$

$$\text{mass} \atop \% B \xleftarrow{\text{100-g sample}} \text{mass} \atop \text{of } B \xleftarrow{\text{AM}} \text{number of} \atop \text{moles of } B$$

The atomic mass (AM), molar mass (MM), and formula mass (FM) of substances involved are the sources of the conversion factors necessary for the indicated steps. In addition, the subscripts in a chemical formula provide us with another conversion factor. For example, given the general formula A_xB_y, we can write the equivalence statement, x mol of $A = y$ mol of B. If the ratio x/y is an integer, we can derive the empirical formula directly: $(AB)_{x/y}$.

The concept of mass percent is used to convert chemical composition data presented in terms of mass percentages to data expressed as masses in grams. Using a 100-g sample as the basis for our calculations eliminates the units we don't want, as illustrated by the following examples.

Example 1: Ethylene is the plant hormone responsible for the ripening of fruit. It is also the starting material for many plastics, such as polyethylene and polystyrene. Ethylene is 85.63% C and 14.37% H, and has a molar mass of 28.05 g mol^{-1}. What are the empirical formula and the molecular formula for ethylene?

Answer: The path is from left to right along the route map shown above.

85.63% C = 85.63 g C/100 g ethylene; 14.37% H = 14.37 g H/100 g ethylene

$$\text{number of} \atop \text{moles of C} = 100 \text{ g ethylene} \left(\frac{85.63 \text{ g C}}{100 \text{ g ethylene}}\right)\left(\frac{1 \text{ mol C}}{12.01 \text{ g C}}\right) = 7.13 \text{ mol C}$$

$$\text{number of} \atop \text{moles of H} = 100 \text{ g ethylene} \left(\frac{14.37 \text{ g H}}{100 \text{ g ethylene}}\right)\left(\frac{1 \text{ mol H}}{1.008 \text{ g H}}\right) = 14.26 \text{ mol H}$$

Number of moles of H/number of moles of C = 14.26 mol$_H$/7.13 mol$_C$ = 2.00 mol$_H$/mol$_C$. This yields the empirical formula, CH_2.

$$\text{molar mass} = 12.01 \text{ g mol}^{-1} + (2 \times 1.008 \text{ g mol}^{-1}) = 14.03 \text{ g mol}^{-1}$$

$$\text{molecular} \atop \text{formula} = \text{empirical} \atop \text{formula} \left(\frac{1 \text{ mol CH}_2}{14.03 \text{ g}}\right)\left(\frac{28.06 \text{ g}}{1 \text{ mol molecules}}\right) = CH_2 \frac{2 \text{ mol CH}_2}{1 \text{ mol molecules}} = (CH_2)_2 = C_2H_4$$

Example 2: Determine the percent composition of ethylene glycol, $C_2H_6O_2$, a common component of antifreeze. MM of $C_2H_6O_2$ is 62.07 g mol^{-1}.

Answer: The path is from right to left along the route map.

$$\%\,C = \left(\frac{2\,\text{mol C}}{1\,\text{mol glycol}}\right)\left(\frac{12.01\,\text{g C}}{1\,\text{mol C}}\right)\left(\frac{1\,\text{mol glycol}}{62.07\,\text{g glycol}}\right)(100\%) = 38.70\%$$

$$\%\,H = \left(\frac{6\,\text{mol H}}{1\,\text{mol glycol}}\right)\left(\frac{1.008\,\text{g H}}{1\,\text{mol H}}\right)\left(\frac{1\,\text{mol glycol}}{62.07\,\text{g glycol}}\right)(100\%) = 9.74\%$$

$$\%\,O = \left(\frac{2\,\text{mol O}}{1\,\text{mol glycol}}\right)\left(\frac{16.00\,\text{g O}}{1\,\text{mol O}}\right)\left(\frac{1\,\text{mol glycol}}{62.07\,\text{g glycol}}\right)(100\%) = 51.55\%$$

Example 3: The oxidation of 50.0 g of manganese produces 79.1 g of an oxide. Calculate (a) the percent composition and (b) the empirical formula of this oxide.

Answer (a):

mass of $A \rightarrow$ mass% A 	 mass of $B \rightarrow$ mass% B

$$\left(\frac{50.0\,\text{g Mn}}{79.1\,\text{g oxide}}\right)(100\%) = 63.2\%\,\text{Mn}; \quad \left(\frac{29.1\,\text{g O}}{79.1\,\text{g oxide}}\right)(100\%) = 36.8\%\,O$$

Answer (b):

mass of $A \rightarrow$ number of moles of A

$\uparrow$
subscripts in formula
$\downarrow$

mass of $B \rightarrow$ number of moles of B

$$\text{number of moles of Mn} = 50.0\,\text{g Mn}\left(\frac{1\,\text{mol Mn}}{54.94\,\text{g Mn}}\right) = 0.91\,\text{mol Mn}$$

$$\text{number of moles of O} = 29.1\,\text{g O}\left(\frac{1\,\text{mol O}}{16.00\,\text{g O}}\right) = 1.82\,\text{mol O}$$

Then, we can calculate number of moles of O/number of moles of Mn = 1.82 mol$_O$/0.91 mol$_{Mn}$ = 2.00 mol$_O$/mol$_{Mn}$. This yields the empirical formula, MnO_2.

Example 4: Oxidation of 10.0 g of aluminum produces 18.9 g of an aluminum oxide. Calculate (a) the percent composition and (b) the empirical formula of this oxide.

Answer (a):

mass of $A \rightarrow$ mass% A 	 mass of $B \rightarrow$ mass% B

$$\left(\frac{10.0\,\text{g Al}}{18.9\,\text{g oxide}}\right)(100\%) = 52.9\%\,\text{Al}; \quad \left(\frac{8.9\,\text{g O}}{18.9\,\text{g oxide}}\right)(100\%) = 47.1\%\,O$$

Answer (b):

$$\text{mass of } A \rightarrow \begin{matrix}\text{number of}\\ \text{moles of } A\end{matrix}$$

$$\uparrow$$

$$\text{subscripts in formula}$$

$$\downarrow$$

$$\text{mass of } B \rightarrow \begin{matrix}\text{number of}\\ \text{moles of } B\end{matrix}$$

$$\begin{matrix}\text{number of}\\ \text{moles of Al}\end{matrix} = 10.0\,\text{g Al}\left(\frac{1\,\text{mol Al}}{27.0\,\text{g Al}}\right) = 0.37\,\text{mol Al}$$

$$\begin{matrix}\text{number of}\\ \text{moles of O}\end{matrix} = 8.9\,\text{g O}\left(\frac{1\,\text{mol O}}{16.00\,\text{g O}}\right) = 0.556\,\text{mol O}$$

We can calculate number of moles of O/number of moles of Al = 0.556 mol_O/0.370 mol_{Al} = 1.50 $\text{mol}_O/\text{mol}_{Al}$. This yields the empirical formula ($Al_{1.0}O_{1.5}$). But all subscripts must be whole numbers, so we multiply the subscripts in the empirical formula subscripts by 2 to give the correct empirical formula Al_2O_3, $(Al_{1.0}O_{1.5})(2)$.

PROBLEM SET 3

3.1 Determine the empirical and molecular formulas of the following substances:

(a) hydrogen peroxide; 5.94% H, 94.06% O; MM = 34.01 g mol^{-1}

(b) disilane; 9.73% H, 90.27% Si; MM = 62.23 g mol^{-1}

(c) benzoyl peroxide; 69.42% C, 4.16% H, 26.42% O; MM = 242.22 g mol^{-1}

(d) phosphorus sulfide; 27.87% P, 72.13% S; MM = 444.58 g mol^{-1}

(e) disulfiram (Antabuse); 40.50% C, 6.80% H, 9.45% N, 43.25% S; MM = 296.54 g mol^{-1}

(f) alumina; 52.91% Al, 47.08% O; MM = 101.96 g mol^{-1}

3.2 Determine the percent composition of the following compounds:

(a) BF_3 (b) KCN   (c) $BaSO_4$

(d) $Ni(CO)_4$ (e) $(NH_4)_2Cr_2O_7$

IV. Reaction Stoichiometry and Balanced Equations

The coefficients in a *balanced* chemical equation can be used to write conversion factors. For example, the general equation, $xA + yB \rightarrow zC$, yields the following equivalence statement:

$$x \text{ mol of } A = y \text{ mol of } B = z \text{ mol of } C$$

The general route for calculating the amounts of materials that react or are produced by the reaction described by this equation is:

$$\text{mass of } A \xleftarrow{\text{AM, MM, or FM}} \begin{matrix}\text{number of}\\ \text{moles of } A\end{matrix} \xleftarrow{\substack{\text{coefficients}\\ \text{in equations}}} \begin{matrix}\text{number of}\\ \text{moles of } B\end{matrix} \xleftarrow{\text{AM, MM, or FM}} \begin{matrix}\text{mass}\\ \text{of } B\end{matrix}$$

Example 1: Ammonia is prepared by the Haber process, which combines nitrogen and hydrogen gases in a reaction described by the equation:

$$N_2(g) + 3\ H_2(g) \rightarrow 2\ NH_3(g)$$

What mass of hydrogen is necessary to completely react 50.0 g N_2?

Answer:

$$g\ N_2 \rightarrow \begin{array}{c}\text{number of}\\ \text{moles of }N_2\end{array} \rightarrow \begin{array}{c}\text{number of}\\ \text{moles of }H_2\end{array} \rightarrow g\ H_2$$

$$\begin{array}{c}\text{mass}\\ \text{of }H_2\end{array} = 50.0\ \text{g}\,N_2 \left(\frac{1\ \text{mol }N_2}{28.02\ \text{g}\,N_2}\right)\left(\frac{3\ \text{mol }H_2}{1\ \text{mol }N_2}\right)\left(\frac{2.02\ \text{g}\,H_2}{1\ \text{mol }H_2}\right) = 10.8\ \text{g}\,H_2$$

Example 2: Given 35.0 g N_2 and 35.0 g H_2 reacting according to the equation in Example 1, which material will react completely, and which will be present in excess? How much NH_3 will be formed?

Answer:

$$\begin{array}{c}\text{mass of }H_2\text{ needed to}\\ \text{completely react 35.0 g }N_2\end{array} = 35.0\ \text{g}\,N_2 \left(\frac{1\ \text{mol }N_2}{28.02\ \text{g}\,N_2}\right)\left(\frac{3\ \text{mol }H_2}{1\ \text{mol }N_2}\right)\left(\frac{2.02\ \text{g}\,H_2}{1\ \text{mol }H_2}\right) = 7.57\ \text{g}\,H_2$$

Thus, there is an excess of H_2 (35.0 g H_2 available) and N_2 is the limiting reactant. The amount of NH_3 formed is dictated by the amount of N_2, the amount of the limiting reactant.

$$\begin{array}{c}\text{mass of}\\ NH_3\text{ formed}\end{array} = 35.0\ \text{g}\,N_2 \left(\frac{1\ \text{mol }N_2}{28.02\ \text{g}\,N_2}\right)\left(\frac{2\ \text{mol }NH_3}{1\ \text{mol }N_2}\right)\left(\frac{17.03\ \text{g }NH_3}{1\ \text{mol }NH_3}\right) = 42.5\ \text{g}\,NH_3$$

PROBLEM SET 4

4.1 For each of the following balanced equations, calculate the mass of the second reactant needed to completely react with 100 g of the first reactant.

(a) $2\,K(s) + 2\,H_2O(g) \rightarrow 2\,KOH(aq) + H_2(g)$

(b) $2\,Al(s) + 3\,F_2(g) \rightarrow 2\,AlF_3(s)$

(c) $4\,NH_3(g) + 5\,O_2(g) \rightarrow 4\,NO(g) + 6\,H_2O(g)$

(d) $Fe_2O_3(s) + 3\,C(s) \rightarrow 2\,Fe(l) + 3\ CO(g)$

(e) $CaC_2(s) + 2\,H_2O(l) \rightarrow Ca(OH)_2(s) + C_2H_2(g)$

(f) $SiO_2(s) + 4\,HF(g) \rightarrow SiF_4(g) + 2\,H_2O(l)$

(g) $2\,C_4H_{10}(g) + 13\,O_2(g) \rightarrow 8\,CO_2(g) + 10\,H_2O(g)$

(h) $BaCl_2(aq) + Na_2SO_4(aq) \rightarrow 2\ NaCl(aq) + BaSO_4(s)$

4.2 Given 100.0 g of each reactant in the reactions described by the preceding equations, which reactant is the limiting reactant, and what mass of the first product listed will be formed?

V. Solution Concentrations and Volumes

Solutions are an important part of chemistry, and we need to perform a variety of calculations when dealing with solutions. For example, we may need to calculate the volume of a solution, in order to obtain the number of moles of solute necessary for a reaction. Or we may need to prepare a specific volume of solution containing a certain number of moles of solute. Or perhaps we need to calculate the change in concentration accompanying a change in the volume of a solution. The relationships necessary to solve problems of this sort are all related to **molarity (M)**, which is the number of moles of solute per liter of solution.

A general route for converting among the various units associated with solutions is shown below:

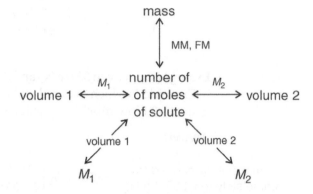

Example 1: What volume of 0.050M NaCl solution contains 15 g of NaCl?

Answer:

mass NaCl → number of moles of NaCl → volume NaCl

$$\text{volume NaCl, L} = 15 \,\cancel{\text{g NaCl}} \left(\frac{1 \,\cancel{\text{mol NaCl}}}{58.4 \,\cancel{\text{g NaCl}}} \right) \left(\frac{1 \text{L}}{0.050 \,\cancel{\text{mol NaCl}}} \right) = 5.1 \text{L}$$

Example 2: How much HCl is required to prepare exactly 250 mL of a 0.150M solution?

Answer:

M of HCl → number of moles of HCl → mass HCl

$$\text{mass HCl, g} = 250 \,\cancel{\text{mL solution}} \left(\frac{0.150 \,\cancel{\text{mol HCl}}}{1 \,\cancel{\text{L solution}}} \right) \left(\frac{1 \,\cancel{\text{L}}}{1000 \,\cancel{\text{mL}}} \right) \left(\frac{36.5 \text{ g HCl}}{1 \,\cancel{\text{mol HCl}}} \right) = 1.37 \text{ g HCl}$$

Note that the use of dimensional analysis in the preceding answer prevented an error of a factor of 10^3, by reminding us to change mL to L so that the units cancel properly.

Example 3: If 100.0 mL of a 0.100M solution of KCl is diluted to 250.0 mL, what is the new concentration of the solution?

Answer: The route shows that the common link between M_1 and M_2 is the number of moles of solute. Set up your calculation this way: M_1 → number of moles → M_2. Note that to get from M_1 to number of moles, we must **multiply** by volume, but to get from number of moles to M_2, we must **divide** by volume.

$$\text{new concentration of KCl} = \left(\frac{0.100 \text{ mol KCl}}{1\text{L solution}_1}\right)(100.0 \text{ mL solution}_1)\left(\frac{1}{250.0 \text{ mL solution}_2}\right) = 0.0400M$$

Because the mL cancel, it is not necessary to convert mL to L in this case. For chemical reactions in solution, the general route for calculations is:

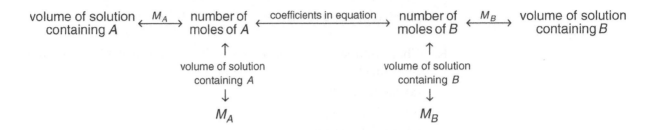

Example 4: For the reaction,

$$KOH(aq) + HCl(aq) \rightarrow KCl(aq) + H_2O(l)$$

what volume of 0.150*M* KOH is required to react completely with 50.00 mL of 0.300*M* HCl?

Answer: The route to follow is:

$$\text{volume of HCl solution} \rightarrow \text{number of moles of HCl} \rightarrow \text{number of moles of KOH} \rightarrow \text{volume of KOH solution}$$

$$\text{volume of KOH solution, mL} = 50.00 \text{ mL HCl}\left(\frac{1\text{L}}{1000 \text{ mL}}\right)\left(\frac{0.300 \text{ mol HCl}}{1\text{L solution}}\right)\left(\frac{1 \text{ mol KOH}}{1 \text{ mol HCl}}\right)\left(\frac{1\text{L solution}}{0.150 \text{ mol KOH}}\right)\left(\frac{1000 \text{ mL}}{1\text{L}}\right) = 100.0 \text{ mL}$$

Example 5: For the reaction

$$2\,NaOH(aq) + H_2SO_4(aq) \rightarrow Na_2SO_4(aq) + 2\,H_2O(\ell)$$

4.5 mL of 0.100*M*H$_2$SO$_4$ is required to completely react with 10.0 mL of a NaOH solution. What is the concentration of the NaOH solution?

Answer: The route to follow is:

$$\text{volume of H}_2\text{SO}_4 \text{ solution} \rightarrow \text{number of moles of H}_2\text{SO}_4 \rightarrow \text{number of moles of NaOH} \rightarrow M \text{ of NaOH solution}$$

$$M \text{ of NaOH solution, } M = \frac{\text{number of moles of NaOH}}{1 \text{L NaOH solution}} = \frac{0.0045 \text{ L}}{\text{H}_2\text{SO}_4 \text{ solution}}\left(\frac{0.100 \text{ mol H}_2\text{SO}_4}{1\text{L H}_2\text{SO}_4 \text{ solution}}\right)\left(\frac{2 \text{ mol NaOH}}{1 \text{ mol H}_2\text{SO}_4}\right)\left(\frac{1}{0.0100 \text{ L NaOH solution}}\right) = 0.090M$$

Note that dimensional analysis reminded us that 2 mol of NaOH react with 1 mol of H$_2$SO$_4$.

PROBLEM SET 5

5.1 Calculate the new concentration of the solution when:

(a) 25.0 mL of 1.43M HCl is diluted to 500.0 mL.

(b) 10.0 mL of 3.42M NaOH is diluted to 10.0 L.

(c) 450.0 mL of 0.20M H_2SO_4 is evaporated to a volume of 90.0 mL.

(d) 60.0 mL of 0.450M NaCl is diluted to 90.0 mL.

5.2 What volume of each of the following solutions contains 0.150 mol of the solute?

(a) 0.0025M HCl

(b) 1.25M $ZnSO_4$

(c) 17.5M NH_4OH

(d) 0.100M $CuCl_2$

5.3 What volume of 0.250M $Ba(OH)_2$ is required to completely react 100.0 mL of a 0.500M solution of the acid in each of the following reactions?

(a) $Ba(OH)_2(aq) + 2\ HCl(aq) \rightarrow BaCl_2(aq) + 2\ H_2O(l)$

(b) $Ba(OH)_2(aq) + H_2SO_4(aq) \rightarrow BaSO_4(aq) + 2\ H_2O(l)$

(c) $Ba(OH)_2(aq) + H_3PO_4(aq) \rightarrow BaHPO_4(aq) + 2\ H_2O(l)$

(d) $3\ Ba(OH)_2(aq) + 2\ H_3PO_4(aq) \rightarrow Ba_3(PO_4)_2(s) + 6\ H_2O(l)$

5.4 In each of the following acid–base reactions, 25.0 mL of an HCl solution (the acid) completely reacts 10.0 mL of a 0.100M solution of the second reactant (the base). Calculate the concentration of the HCl solution in each case.

(a) $HCl(aq) + NH_4OH(aq) \rightarrow NH_4Cl(aq) + H_2O(l)$

(b) $2\ HCl(aq) + Ca(OH)_2(aq) \rightarrow CaCl_2(aq) + 2\ H_2O(l)$

(c) $4\ HCl(aq) + NaAl(OH)_4(aq) \rightarrow AlCl_3(aq) + 4\ H_2O(l) + NaCl(aq)$

(d) $2\ HCl(aq) + Na_2C_2O_4(aq) \rightarrow 2\ NaCl(aq) + H_2C_2O_4(aq)$

Answers to Problem Sets

Problem Set 1

1.1 655.72 hr

1.2 215.9 cm

1.3 603 cm^2

1.4 6.8×10^7 min

1.5 0.53 gal

1.6 1.13 kg

1.7 6.06×10^{-9} in

1.8 422 ft, 129 m

1.9 62 mi hr^{-1}

1.10 472 mL

1.11 8.604 lb gal^{-1}

1.12 3820. km

1.13 37.7 mi hr^{-1}

1.14 41.5 lb

1.15 20.5 in. Hg, 0.686 atm, 6.95×10^4 Pa

1.16 1.07×10^3 mi hr^{-1}

1.17 1.89 mg F^-

1.18 322 min

1.19 5679 °F

1.20 0.697 g mL^{-1}

1.21 425 kg, 937 lb

1.22 50 °C, 323 K

Problem Set 2

2.1 (a) 2.083 mol **(b)** 1.020 mol **(c)** 0.3224 mol
(d) 0.2921 mol **(e)** 0.5076 mol

2.2 (a) 72 g **(b)** 39 g **(c)** 40 g **(d)** 29 g **(e)** 39 g

2.3 (a) 3.764×10^{24} ions
(b) 1.882×10^{24} molecules
(c) 1.494×10^{24} molecules
(d) 3.101×10^{23} molecules
(e) 1.210×10^{23} molecules

2.4 (a) 5.66 g **(b)** 53.8 g **(c)** 59.5 g **(d)** 96.7 g **(e)** 45.5 g

Problem Set 3

3.1 (a) HO, H_2O_2 **(b)** SiH_3, Si_2H_6
(c) $C_7H_5O_2$, $C_{14}H_{10}O_4$ **(d)** P_2S_5, P_4S_{10}
(e) $C_5H_{10}NS_2$, $C_{10}H_{20}N_2S_4$
(f) Al_2O_3, Al_2O_3

3.2 (a) 15.95% B, 84.05% F
(b) 60.04% K, 18.45% C, 21.51% N
(c) 58.84% Ba, 13.74% S, 27.42% O
(d) 34.38% Ni, 28.14% C, 37.48% O
(e) 11.11% N, 3.20% H, 41.26% Cr, 44.43% O

Problem Set 4

4.1 (a) 46.08 g **(b)** 211.2 g **(c)** 234.9 g
(d) 22.56 g **(e)** 56.21 g **(f)** 133.2 g
(g) 357.9 g **(h)** 68.20 g

4.2 (a) K, 143.5 **(b)** F_2, 147.3 g
(c) O_2, 75.02 g **(d)** Fe_2O_3, 69.94 g
(e) CaC_2, 115.6g **(f)** HF, 130.1 g
(g) O_2, 84.64 g **(h)** $BaCl_2$, 56.13 g

Problem Set 5

5.1 (a) 0.0715*M* (b) 0.00342*M* (c) 1.00*M*
(d) 0.300*M*

5.2 (a) 60.0 L (b) 0.120 L or 120 mL
(c) 0.00857 L or 8.57 mL (d) 1.50 L

5.3 (a) 100.0 mL (b) 200.0 mL (c) 200.0 mL
(d) 300.0 mL

5.4 (a) 0.0400*M* (b) 0.0800*M* (c) 0.160*M*
(d) 0.0800*M*

Representing Data Graphically

Prepared by Norman E. Griswold, Nebraska Wesleyan University

PURPOSE OF THE EXPERIMENT

Learn basic features of graphs, with emphasis on line graphs. Prepare line graphs by choosing appropriate graphic format. Become familiar with common types of line graphs used in general chemistry.

BACKGROUND INFORMATION

Scientists answer scientific questions by doing experiments, which provide information about a given problem. After collecting enough experimental information, scientists attempt to correlate the observed data and derive fundamental relationships. Frequently, graphical representations of the data help make the relationships among data more easily understood. Scientists can also use graphs to predict or estimate information that is difficult to determine experimentally.

A **graph** is a diagram that represents the variation of one system factor in relation to the resulting variation of one or more other factors. Figure 1 on the next page shows three different types of graphs. The simplest and most widely used type for plotting scientific data is the line graph.

We use **line graphs** to compare the values of two variables. We represent these variables using scales on two straight lines called **axes**. The vertical axis is the **y-axis**, or **ordinate**, and the horizontal axis is the **x-axis**, or **abscissa**. We label each axis with a numerical scale. The numbers on the y-axis represent values of one variable, and the numbers on the x-axis represent values of a second variable. In conventional line graphs, scale values increase when reading upward on the y-axis and to the right on the x-axis, as shown in Figure 2 on the next page.

For example, if you were cooling a liquid and constantly monitoring its temperature, the temperature would decrease every second until the liquid froze. Based on the temperature–time data collected, you could see how the temperature changed with time, by graphing the data. You would plot temperature on the y-axis and time on the x-axis, as shown in Figure 3 on the next page.

If the axes of a line graph intersect at the point where the numbers on both axes are zero, we call this point the **origin**. We determine the points to be plotted on a graph, called **data points**, by pairing the values of one variable with the corresponding values of the other variable. We represent

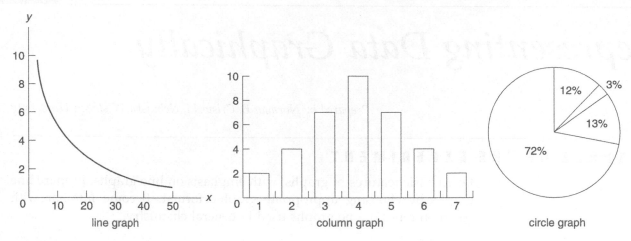

Figure 1
Three types of graphs

data points using the form (x, y) where x is the value of the variable plotted on the x-axis, and y is the corresponding value of the other variable.

For example, suppose you have a group of data in which the y variable is 20 when the x variable is 25. You would plot this data point by placing a dot on the graph at a position that is directly across from 20 on the y-axis and directly above 25 on the x-axis. In Figure 4, data point P represents the data point (25, 20).

We can also plot negative values on line graphs. For example, in Figure 4, data point Q represents the data point $(-20, -15)$, at which $x = -20$ and $y = -15$.

A line graph consists of a set of data points through which a smooth curve or straight line has been drawn that best represents all of the data points. Consider the data table in Figure 5, which shows the Celsius temperatures that are equivalent to selected Fahrenheit temperatures. Figure 5(a) shows a plot of these data. A straight line drawn through these data points represents the relationship between the two temperature scales, as you can

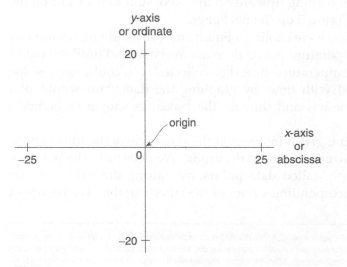

Figure 2
The x-axis and y-axis of a line graph

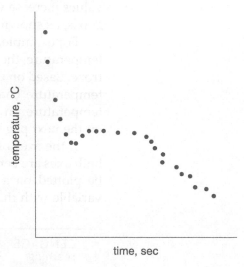

Figure 3
Plot of temperature versus time for a cooling liquid

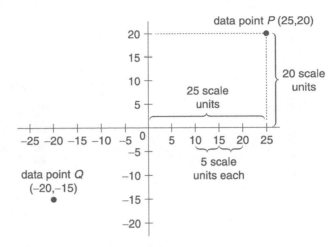

Figure 4
Plotting a data point on a line graph

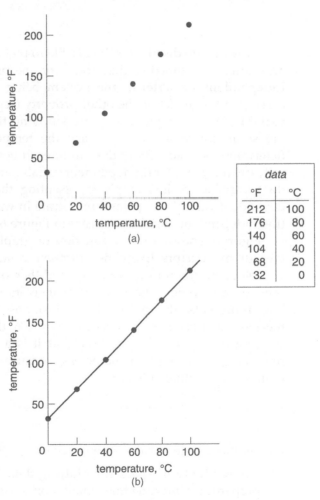

data	
°F	°C
212	100
176	80
140	60
104	40
68	20
32	0

Figure 5
Creating a line graph: (a) data points plotted; (b) data represented by a straight line

see in Figure 5(b). Note that the line does not pass through the origin. Instead, it crosses the y-axis at the point representing the values $x = 0$ °C and $y = 32$ °F. In any line graph, the value of y when $x = 0$ is known as the **y-intercept**.

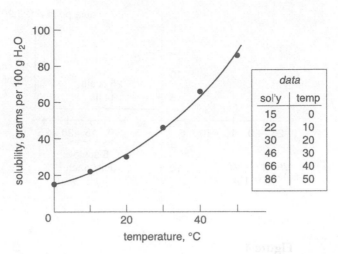

Figure 6
A line graph of the solubility of potassium nitrate in water at various temperatures

How do you decide which variable to plot on which axis? Experiments are normally planned so that you vary one property (represented by the **independent variable)** of the system being studied, then measure the corresponding effect on the other property (represented by the **dependent variable**). For example, if you are studying the effect of temperature on the solubility of a salt, you vary the temperature of the system and determine the solubility of the salt at each new temperature. We customarily use the y-axis for the dependent variable and the x-axis for the independent variable. A line graph representing the measured solubility (the dependent variable) of potassium nitrate in water at various temperatures (the independent variable) appears in Figure 6.

Figure 6 shows another function of graphs, which is to average out measurement errors. Every measurement contains some degree of error. If you plot a group of measured data and then draw the line that best represents the data points, the measurement errors are averaged out. That is, the line represents the most likely positions of the data points, with measurement errors minimized. In Figure 6, the line passes through only the first data point. You can see that it is a good representation of the remaining data points, nonetheless, because roughly equal numbers of points fall on either side of it.

PROCEDURE

I. Preparing a Line Graph

Follow these general rules when preparing a line graph.

1. **Allow plenty of space for plotting data**. Larger graphs are easier to prepare and interpret than smaller ones. Use an entire $8.5 \times 11''$ sheet of graph paper for each graph so that the graph is large. The data points should be distributed so that the resulting straight line or smooth curve extends throughout the entire page, instead of being confined to a small portion of the paper (see Rule 4).

2. **Draw the axes using a ruler or other straightedge**. Allow space for labels along the left-hand side of the y-axis and under the x-axis.

3. **Determine which property to plot on which axis.** Assign the dependent variable to the y-axis and the independent variable to the x-axis.

4. **Determine what numerical scale to use on each axis. Consider the following sample data.**

x	40	41	42	43	44
y	50	55	60	65	70

When plotting these data, if you make the intersection of your axes the origin, and use identical scales on both axes, you will obtain the straight line graph shown in Figure 7(a). Interpretation of this graph is difficult, both because the line is short, and because the line is in an upper corner of the graph, far from the axes.

How can you alter the scales so that the resulting line graph will be longer, hence, easier to interpret? You can begin by making the axes intersect at the point where $x = 40$ and $y = 50$, so that the line graph will begin at the intersection of the axes. Then, by expanding the size of the scale units on both axes, you can make the resulting line graph extend over a larger area, as shown in Figure 7(b). This graph uses more of the y-axis, but still uses only a fraction of the x-axis. You can further improve the usefulness of this graph if you expand the scale on the x-axis even more. This last change will produce the graph shown in Figure 7(c). This graph is easy to prepare and to interpret because it is large and makes efficient use of both axes. You should construct all your graphs in this way, so that the lines or curves are as long as possible.

After you have chosen your scales and scale unit sizes, mark the axes. Use the lines on your graph paper to count off scale units. To avoid wasting time and space, do not number individual scale units. Instead, select some convenient multiple, such as 5 or 10 units, and mark only

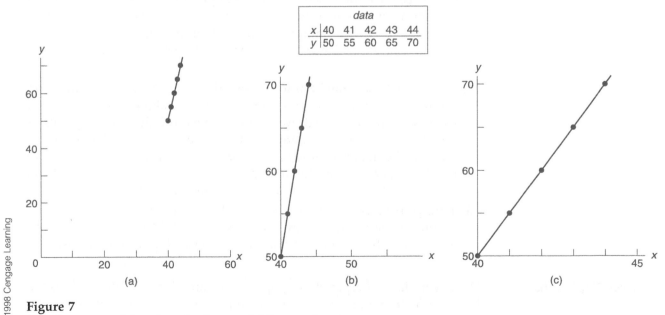

Figure 7
Selecting appropriate axis scales for a useful line graph

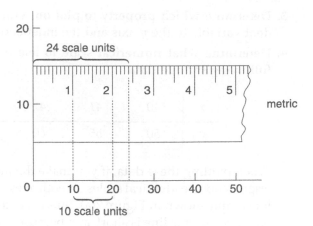

Figure 8
Using a metric ruler to measure individual scale units

these values at the appropriate intervals. If you are using graph paper with lines that are 1 centimeter apart, you can let the space between lines equal 10 scale units. You can then use a metric ruler to measure individual scale units, because each centimeter on the ruler is divided into 10 millimeters (see Figure 8).

If you cannot make efficient use of your graph paper by using scale intervals representing either 5 or 10 units, at least let the space between graph paper lines represent an even number of units. This will make it easier for you to divide the space between lines into parts when plotting data points that do not fall on a graph paper line.

5. **Label each axis**. After you have numbered the axis scales, label each axis clearly with the property it represents and the corresponding units. Proper axis labels appear in Figure 6, where the label for the *y*-axis is "solubility, grams per 100 grams H_2O", and the label for the *x*-axis is "temperature, °C".

6. **Organize the data in tabular form, and plot the data points**. Several of the figures in this module include data tables written on the graphs. You should set up a similar table for each graph you construct. Plot the data, as shown in Figure 4, making small dark points for each data point.

7. **Draw the best straight line or smooth curve to represent the data points**. If the data points visually indicate a straight-line graph, use a ruler or straightedge to draw a straight line through as many points as possible, with about as many points on one side of the line as on the other. If the data points suggest a curved line, draw the smooth curve that best represents all the data points, with about as many points on one side of the curve as on the other, as shown in Figure 6.

8. **Title your graph**. A title helps to quickly communicate the data that a graph represents. If you are preparing several different graphs for an experiment, titles will help you distinguish each graph more easily.

II. Interpreting Graphs

Once you have prepared a graph, you can obtain additional useful information from it. For example, sometimes you can determine data points outside the range of those plotted. You may be able to determine other

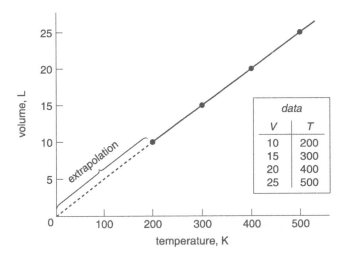

Figure 9
Extrapolation of a straight-line graph

information, based on the shape of the curve. In this section, you will begin by learning how to interpret straight-line graphs. Then you will move on to the interpretation of some curved-line (non-linear) graphs.

A. Straight-Line Graphs

We can easily extend, or **extrapolate**, a straight-line graph to include data points that were not determined experimentally. In Figure 9, for example, the straight line has been extrapolated to the origin. This technique allows us to determine additional points that were not part of the original data. It also enables us to determine the y-intercept of the graph, which we use to express the equation of the graph. In this case, the y-intercept is zero.

All straight line graphs can be described by the general equation

$$y = mx + b \qquad \text{(Eq. 1)}$$

in which x and y are variables, and m and b are constants. For example, if we let $m = 4$ and $b = 3$, Equation 1 becomes:

$$y = 4x + 3 \qquad \text{(Eq. 2)}$$

In the general equation, b is the y-intercept of the line, and m is the slope of the line.

We can obtain a graph of Equation 2 in the following way. We substitute a range of values, such as 1, 2, and 3, for x in Equation 2. We then solve the resulting equations for y, as shown in Table 1. The corresponding pairs of values for x and y are plotted in Figure 10 on the next page.

In Figure 10, the y-intercept is $y = 3$, so $b = 3$ in the equation for this line. This relationship between the value of b and the y-intercept holds true for all straight-line graphs.

We can determine the slope of the line, m, by dividing the difference (Δy) between the y values ($\Delta y = y_2 - y_1$) of any two points on the line by the difference (Δx) between the corresponding x values ($\Delta x = x_2 - x_1$).

Table 1 *Values for x and y in the equation $y = 4x + 3$*

if $x =$	the equation becomes	and $y =$
0	$y = 4(0) + 3$	3
1	$y = 4(1) + 3$	7
2	$y = 4(2) + 3$	11
3	$y = 4(3) + 3$	15

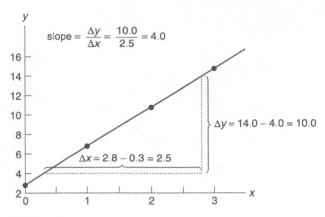

Figure 10
Graph of the Data in Table 1

Because the line is the best representation of *all* of the data, we *use values of points on the line, rather than experimentally determined data points, to determine the slope*. In order to obtain more significant figures in the calculated slope, we use widely separated points on the line for our determination.

The determination of the slope of the line in Figure 10 is shown mathematically in Equation 3, as well as in the figure itself.

$$\text{slope} = \frac{\Delta y}{\Delta x} = \frac{14.0 - 4.0}{2.8 - 0.3} = \frac{10.0}{2.5} = 4.0 \qquad \text{(Eq. 3)}$$

To mathematically prove that the slope of any straight line is a constant, we can recalculate the slope of the line in Figure 10, using different points on the line, as shown in Equation 4. The result matches that of Equation 3, confirming that the slope is a constant.

$$\text{slope} = \frac{\Delta y}{\Delta x} = \frac{12.0 - 8.0}{2.3 - 1.3} = \frac{4.0}{1.0} = 4.0 \qquad \text{(Eq. 4)}$$

In the above example, we used a slope equation to determine data for a graph. However, we often use the reverse process. In such cases, experiments are performed, and the observed data are plotted. If a straight-line graph is obtained, the slope and intercept can be determined directly from the graph. Then an equation, such as $y = 4x + 3$, can be derived to represent the relationship shown by the graph.

B. Examples of Linear Relationships

Straight-line graphs can represent the relationships of some factors that we use in chemistry.

1. **Temperature conversion**. We can convert temperatures on the Celsius scale, °C, to the equivalent temperatures on the Fahrenheit scale, °F, using Equation 5.

$$°F = \frac{9}{5}°C + 32 \qquad \text{(Eq. 5)}$$

This equation has the same basic form as Equation 1, with °F corresponding to y, and °C corresponding to x. The y-intercept of the graph associated with this equation (*b* in Equation 1) is 32, as shown in Figure 5. We can use this graph to directly convert between Fahrenheit and equivalent Celsius temperatures, without having to individually calculate each conversion using Equation 5.

2. Gas laws. We can express one of the gas laws, Charles' law, as

$$V = kT \qquad \text{(Eq. 6)}$$

where V represents volume, T represents absolute temperature, and k is a constant. This equation is also in the form $y = mx + b$, where $y = V$, $x = T$, $m = k$, and $b = 0$. A graph illustrating Charles' law consists of a plot of gas volume versus absolute temperature, as shown in Figure 9. Interpreting this graph, we can reach the following conclusions:

   a. We can clearly see the direct proportionality of V to T. For example, when T doubles, V doubles.

   b. We can obtain the value of the constant, k, by calculating the slope of the line.

   c. The line has been extrapolated to intersect the y-axis at the origin (hence, the y-intercept is zero). This extrapolation was the basis for establishing zero on the Kelvin scale.

We can express another gas law, Boyle's law, as

$$PV = k \qquad \text{(Eq. 7)}$$

where P represents pressure, V represents gas volume, and k is a constant. Note that this equation is *not* in the form $y = mx + b$. A plot of volume–pressure data for a specific gas sample gives a hyperbolic curve, as shown in Figure 11(a). There are a couple of drawbacks to this graph. First, a large number of data points are required in order to draw this curve accurately.

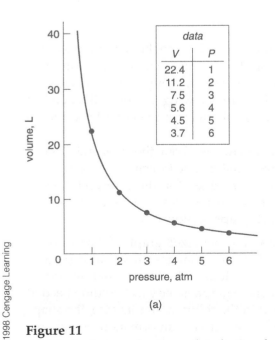

data	
V	P
22.4	1
11.2	2
7.5	3
5.6	4
4.5	5
3.7	6

(a)

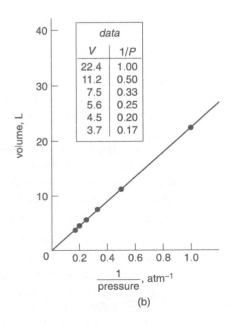

data	
V	1/P
22.4	1.00
11.2	0.50
7.5	0.33
5.6	0.25
4.5	0.20
3.7	0.17

(b)

Figure 11
A plot of volume and pressure data for 1 mol of hydrogen at 0 °C: (a) graph of V vs. P; (b) graph of V vs. 1/P

Second, it is not easy to extrapolate values at the extremes of the curve. However, if you only need to see the general relationship between gas volume and pressure, then this graph is adequate.

If you wish to use extrapolation to determine additional volume–pressure data for the gas sample, or if you wish to determine the value of the constant, k, you can re-express Boyle's law as

$$V = k\frac{1}{P} \qquad \text{(Eq. 8)}$$

Equation 8 has the same form as Equation 1, where

$$V = y, \quad k = m, \quad \frac{1}{P} = x, \quad \text{and } b = 0.$$

A plot of V versus $1/P$ for hydrogen at $0\,°C$ gives a straight line that passes through the origin, as shown in Figure 11(b). This line has a slope equal to k.

3. Reaction Rates. We can express the rates of certain simple reactions using $y = mx + b$ equations. For example, for the reaction

$$PCl_5(g) \rightarrow PCl_3(g) + Cl_2(g)$$

the reaction rate, R, is directly proportional to the molar concentration of PCl_5, expressed as $[PCl_5]$. The mathematical expression for this proportionality, the so-called rate equation, is

$$R = k[PCl_5] \qquad \text{(Eq. 9)}$$

where k is the rate constant. We can use a graph of reaction rate versus molar concentration of reactant to determine the value of the rate constant, because the slope of the line equals k.

C. Curved-Line Graphs

Some chemical relationships are not linear and cannot be converted to such a form. That is, there are no simple linear equations to represent such relationships. A plot of data for this kind of relationship gives a curved-line graph. This type of graph is useful in showing an overall chemical relationship, although the slope and the y-intercept are not relevant to its interpretation.

It is difficult to make general statements about the interpretation of curved-line graphs. However, a directional change in a curved-line graph is often used to derive useful data. Techniques for the interpretation of different kinds of curved-line graphs must be learned as each kind is encountered. Three examples of such graphs follow.

1. **Titration curves**. Figure 12 shows a generalized graph of data from an acid–base titration. The graph distinctly changes direction to become almost vertical at a certain titrant volume. The titrant volume corresponding to the vertical portion of the graph is the exact volume needed to completely neutralize the acid in the solution. In this case, the shape of the curved-line graph provides useful information about the chemical system being studied.

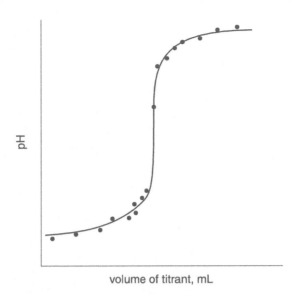

Figure 12
Acid–base titration curve

2. **Cooling curves**. As you may recall, Figure 3 shows a generalized plot of temperature and time for a cooling liquid. The plotted line changes direction and forms a plateau when the temperature reaches the freezing point of the liquid at laboratory pressure. Here again, the shape of the curve provides useful information about the system being studied.

3. **Solubility curves**. Figure 6 shows a third type of curved-line graph, a solubility graph. This type of graph has no sudden directional changes. However, it is useful for determining how much of a substance will dissolve in 100 g H_2O at various temperatures.

II. Using Computers to Plot Graphs

We can easily use computers to prepare graphs. There are a number of software programs available for computerized graphing. However, the software is varied enough that we cannot give specific directions for its use here. Nevertheless, we can make some general statements.

You normally start with a spreadsheet and type data into columns. Then you select the data and click the appropriate command to initiate development of a graph, sometimes called a chart. You drag a marker to indicate the area on the spreadsheet to be occupied by the graph. You can choose the type of graph you want (line, column, pie chart, etc.). Sometimes a crude graph appears at this point. You can add a title, axis labels, and scale values. Finally, you can designate the number of grid lines and make many other alterations to improve the appearance of the graph.

Name _____ Section _____ Date _____

Questions

1. On the following graph, clearly label the

   (a) ordinate

   (b) abscissa

   (c) origin

   (d) y-intercept

   (e) data point (9.0, 10.5)

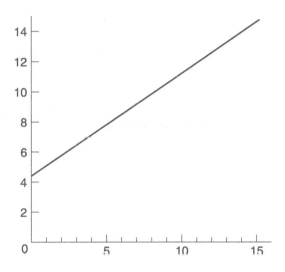

2. The following measurements were made of an oxygen sample at 1.0 atm.

volume, L	temperature, °C
25.00	31.49
30.00	92.38
35.00	153.28
40.00	214.18
45.00	275.08
50.00	335.97

(a) Which property is represented by the independent variable?

(b) Prepare a graph of these data using the graph paper supplied.

(c) Based on your graph, what do you estimate the oxygen volume is at 100.0 °C?

(d) Determine the slope of the line.

(e) If the slope were the same as you calculated in (d) and the y-intercept for this graph were −273.0 °C, write the equation for the line.

Using Statistics to Analyze Experimental Data

Prepared by Peter J. Krieger, Palm Beach Community College

PURPOSE OF THE EXPERIMENT

Measure some physical properties of some common objects. Use statistics to analyze the collected data.

BACKGROUND REQUIRED

You should be familiar with basic laboratory techniques for measuring mass, length, volume, and temperature.

BACKGROUND INFORMATION

We perform experiments in order to investigate and formulate scientific concepts. Many experiments require us to make physical measurements, such as determining the mass of an object. In such cases, we can sometimes use our measurements and observations to predict the results of similar future experiments.

In order to correctly interpret experimental measurements, we need to know how reliable the measurements are. A common technique for obtaining reliable measurements is to perform the same measurement several times, then analyze the data using **statistics**, the application of mathematical principles to a data set.

Experimental Error

Suppose in weighing a clean crucible, we pick up the crucible with our fingers. Handling the crucible in this fashion introduces error into the mass measurement, because oils from the skin are left on the crucible. The balance measures the added mass of these oils, even though their mass is tiny. Thus, the crucible appears to weigh more than it really does. If we weighed several crucibles using this procedure, each crucible would consistently weigh too much. Handling the crucible with fingers introduces **experimental error**. There are two types of experimental error: **systematic** and **random**.

Systematic error is caused by error within the experimental procedure. Because the error is due to the manner in which the experiment is performed, we can reduce or even eliminate the error by simply correcting the procedure. In the preceding example, for instance, we can eliminate the systematic error by handling the crucibles with clean tongs, instead of fingers. Then, when each crucible is weighed, the measurement will be closer to the crucible's actual mass. **Accuracy** is defined as how close a measurement is to the corresponding actual value. The closer a measurement is to the actual value, the more accurate it is. Thus, systematic errors cause inaccurate measurements.

In contrast, **random error** occurs when multiple measurements of the same property differ, despite our best efforts to repeat the measurements in an identical fashion. For example, suppose we use a cloth tape measure to determine the length of a laboratory desk. If we repeat this measurement several times, we may determine a slightly different length each time. This is because the cloth stretches when it is pulled tight, and it is difficult to use the same tension every time. Thus, even proper use of laboratory equipment can result in differing readings when the same measurement is repeated. We need our measurements to be as reproducible as possible, in order to yield precise data. **Precision** is defined as the ability to reproduce the same measurement under the same conditions. Hence, random errors cause a set of repeated measurements to be imprecise.

Example

Problem 1 A student analyzes the acidity of three samples of a vinegar, with a known mass percent acetic acid of 5.00%. The student measures the mass percent acetic acid of the three samples as 6.24%, 6.25%, and 6.24%, respectively. Comment on the precision and accuracy of the student's measurements.

Solution The measurements are reproducible; that is, they are very close to each other. Therefore, they are relatively precise. On the other hand, the measurements are not very close to the actual value, so they are not accurate. This is likely due to systematic error caused by an error in the procedure used for the analysis.

Statistics

The most common statistic used to analyze a set of repeated measurements is the **mean**, or **average**. We calculate the mean by taking the sum, Σ, of the individual measurements, x, and dividing by the number of measurements, n, as shown in Equation 1.

$$\text{mean} = (\Sigma x)/n \qquad\qquad \text{(Eq. 1)}$$

We interpret the mean as the central tendency of the data set. This means that if we were to repeat the measurement once more, we would expect to obtain a value close to the mean.

However, what if the data set includes one or two extremely inaccurate measurements? In such cases, the mean may not accurately reflect the central tendency of the data set. Therefore, as an alternative, we also calculate the **median** of the data set, as follows. We list the measurements in order, from lowest to highest. The median will be the middle one, if there are an odd number of measurements. If there are an even number of measurements, the median will be the mean of the two middle ones.

Given a sufficiently large number of measurements, the median and mean should be equal, or nearly so. If you must use a small number of measurements, the median is sometimes a more accurate reflection of the central tendency of the data than the mean.

We use the mean and the median to try to determine the actual value of the property we have attempted to measure. We define the difference between each measured value and the corresponding actual value as the **error**, shown in Equation 2.

$$error = measured\ value - actual\ value \qquad (Eq.\ 2)$$

The size of the error defines the accuracy of the measurement. Note that, in many cases, the actual value of a property is not known, so the error in a measurement of that property cannot be calculated.

We express the precision of each measurement in a data set as the **deviation** (d) of that measurement from the mean, as shown in Equation 3.

$$deviation\ (d) = measured\ value - mean \qquad (Eq.\ 3)$$

In this manner, we can evaluate each measurement's reproducibility.

Average error and **average deviation** are two more statistical tools we use to determine the accuracy and precision, respectively, of a set of measurements. We define average error as the sum of the absolute values (numerical values without signs) of the errors calculated for all of the measurements divided by the number of measurements. Similarly, we define average deviation as the sum of the absolute values of all of the deviations divided by the number of measurements. The smaller the average error, the more accurate the measurements; the smaller the average deviation, the more precise the measurements.

We can use the statistical tool of **standard deviation** to give us an even better measure of the precision of a data set. Equation 4 illustrates the formula for standard deviation, σ, where d is the deviation of each measurement, and n is the number of measurements.

$$\sigma = [(\Sigma d^2)/(n-1)]^{1/2} \qquad (Eq.\ 4)$$

As shown in the equation, we square the deviation of each measurement, then total the squares, divide the sum by $n - 1$, and take the square root of the result. Given a reasonably large set of measurements, about 95% of the measurements should fall within one standard deviation of the mean, plus or minus.

Small sets of measurements, on the other hand, do not necessarily meet the standard deviation test. Due to chance alone, a small set of data may contain measurements that are quite different from the actual value of the measured property. The mean determined for this small set of data is correspondingly well above or below the mean that would follow from a much larger set of measurements. The result is that a small set of measurements may lead to a wrong conclusion.

Example

Therefore, you should inspect your data carefully, in order to avoid such problems. A chemist's approach is to take as many measurements as reasonable in order to obtain as accurate a mean as possible.

Suppose you measure the length of a car key, using a centimeter ruler. Further, suppose you get four of your friends to make the same measurement, and you list the data in Table 1.

Table 1 *Length of a car key, measured using a ruler*

	measurement				
	1	2	3	4	5
length, cm	5.52	5.50	5.52	5.55	5.54

Problem 2 Determine the mean and the median of this data set.

Solution We use Equation 1 to calculate the mean.

$$\text{mean} = \frac{(5.52 + 5.50 + 5.52 + 5.55 + 5.54)}{5} = 5.53 \text{ cm}$$

Listing the values in ascending order, (5.50, 5.52, 5.52, 5.54, 5.55), the middle entry, or median, is 5.52 cm. Because the median is very close to the mean, we would predict that another person measuring the key would attain a measurement close to 5.53 cm, the mean.

Problem 3 Suppose your instructor then measures this key's length, using calipers, which is a much more accurate measurement tool. The instructor determines that the key is 5.51 cm long. Assuming that this is the actual length of the key, calculate the average error, average deviation, and standard deviation for the measurements in Table 1.

Solution First, we determine the error for each measurement, using Equation 2, as shown in Table 2.

Table 2 *Error for each measurement (error = measured value − actual value)*

measured value, cm	5.52	5.50	5.52	5.55	5.54
error, cm	+0.01	−0.01	+0.01	+0.04	+0.03

We then calculate the average error for all of the measurements.

$$\text{average error} = \frac{(0.01 + 0.01 + 0.01 + 0.04 + 0.03)}{5} = 0.02 \text{ cm}$$

Note that we use the absolute values of the errors for the summation. The average error determines the overall accuracy of the data set. The smaller the average error, the more accurate the measurements.

Next, we calculate the deviation of each measurement from the mean, using Equation 3, as shown in Table 3.

Table 3 *Deviation of each measurement (deviation = measured value − mean)*

measured value, cm	5.52	5.50	5.52	5.55	5.54
deviation, cm	−0.01	−0.03	−0.01	+0.02	+0.01

We then calculate the average deviation for all of the measurements.

$$\text{average deviation} = \frac{(0.01 + 0.03 + 0.01 + 0.02 + 0.01)}{5} = 0.02 \text{ cm}$$

Note, once again, that we use the absolute values of the deviations in the summation. The average deviation determines the overall precision of the data set. The smaller the average deviation, the more precise the measurements.

To determine the standard deviation of the data set, we substitute the individual deviations into Equation 1.

$$\sigma = \{[(-0.01)^2 + (-0.03)^2 + (-0.01)^2 + (0.02)^2 + (0.01)^2]/(5-1)\}^{\frac{1}{2}}$$
$$= [(0.0001 + 0.0009 + 0.0001 + 0.0004 + 0.0001)/4]^{\frac{1}{2}}$$
$$= (0.0016/4)^{\frac{1}{2}}$$
$$= (0.0004)^{\frac{1}{2}}$$
$$= 0.02 \text{ cm}$$

We should expect 95% of all measurements of the car key made using the ruler to be within ±0.02 cm of the mean, 5.53 cm. In other words, we would predict that if another person measured the length of this key with the ruler, they would most likely obtain a measurement between 5.51 and 5.55 cm.

PROCEDURE

CAUTION ⚠

Wear departmentally approved safety goggles while doing this experiment.

NOTE: Record all measurements on your Data Sheet.

Record all measurements using the maximum precision allowed by your equipment. For example, most metric rulers can be read to the nearest 0.01 cm, most graduated cylinders to the nearest 0.1 mL, most electronic balances to either the nearest 0.01 or 0.001 g, and most thermometers to the nearest 0.1 °C.

I. Circumference of a 150-mL Beaker

1. Wrap a piece of string around the circumference of a 150-mL beaker. Pull the string tight, but try not to stretch it. Use a pencil to mark the two points on the string where it crosses itself.

2. Use a ruler to measure the distance between the two marks on the string, in centimeters.

3. Repeat Steps 1 and 2 for nine other 150-mL beakers.

II. Mass, Volume, and Density of Marbles

4. Wash a marble with a detergent solution, rinse, and dry completely.

5. Tare a plastic weighing boat on a balance.

6. Using tongs or lint-free tissue to handle the marble, measure the marble's mass in the tared weighing boat.

7. Fill a 25-mL graduated cylinder about halfway with tap water. Measure this initial volume in milliliters.

8. *Carefully* place the marble in the graduated cylinder. Tap or gently shake the cylinder to dislodge any air bubbles clinging to the marble. Then measure the volume of the marble plus the water, and record it as the final volume.

9. Repeat Steps 4–8 with the same graduated cylinder and nine other marbles.

III. Volume of a Test Tube

10. Obtain a 13 × 100-mm test tube.

11. Completely fill the test tube with tap water, so that the water is level with the top of the tube.

12. Carefully pour the water from the test tube into a dry, 25-mL graduated cylinder. Measure the water volume in milliliters.

13. Repeat Steps 10–12 with the same graduated cylinder and nine other 13 × 100-mm test tubes.

IV. Temperature of Boiling Water

14. Fill a 600-mL beaker approximately three-quarters full with tap water. Set the beaker on a hot plate, as shown in Figure 1. Place a support ring around the beaker, as shown, in order to minimize the chance of upsetting it. Bring the water to a boil.

15. Measure the temperature of the boiling water by using a utility clamp to suspend a thermometer in the boiling water, as shown in Figure 1, for a minimum of 1 min.

16. Repeat Step 15 with nine other thermometers.

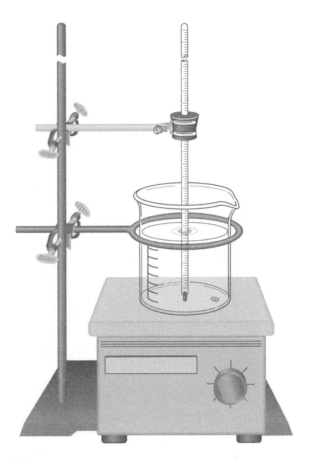

Figure 1
Suspending a thermometer in a beaker of boiling water

CAUTION

Wash your hands thoroughly with soap or detergent before leaving the laboratory.

_____   _____   _____
Name   *Section*   *Date*

Data Sheet

I. Circumference of a 150-mL Beaker

	measurement									
	1	2	3	4	5	6	7	8	9	10
circumference, cm	____	____	____	____	____	____	____	____	____	____

II. Mass, Volume, and Density of Marbles

	measurement									
	1	2	3	4	5	6	7	8	9	10
mass, g	____	____	____	____	____	____	____	____	____	____
final volume, mL	____	____	____	____	____	____	____	____	____	____
initial volume, mL	____	____	____	____	____	____	____	____	____	____
volume of marble*, mL	____	____	____	____	____	____	____	____	____	____
density of marble[†], g/mL	____	____	____	____	____	____	____	____	____	____

* volume of marble = volume of water displaced = final volume − initial volume
[†] density of marble = mass/volume

III. Volume of a Test Tube

	measurement									
	1	2	3	4	5	6	7	8	9	10
volume, mL	____	____	____	____	____	____	____	____	____	____

IV. Temperature of Boiling Water

	measurement									
	1	2	3	4	5	6	7	8	9	10
temperature, °C	____	____	____	____	____	____	____	____	____	____

_____   _____   _____
Name   *Section*   *Date*

Results Sheet

I. Circumference of a 150-mL Beaker

circumference measurements, in ascending order:

circumference, cm   ____   ____   ____   ____   ____   ____   ____   ____   ____   ____
                             smallest   largest

median circumference, cm   _____

mean circumference, cm   _____

average deviation, cm   _____

standard deviation, cm   _____

II. Mass, Volume, and Density of Marbles

masses of marbles, in ascending order:

mass, g   ____   ____   ____   ____   ____   ____   ____   ____   ____   ____
            smallest   largest

median mass, g   _____

mean mass, g   _____

average deviation, g   _____

standard deviation, g   _____

densities of marbles, in ascending order:

density, g/mL   ____   ____   ____   ____   ____   ____   ____   ____   ____   ____
                   smallest   largest

median density, g/mL   _____

mean density, g/mL   _____

average deviation, g/mL   _____

standard deviation, g/mL   _____

average error, g/mL   _____

(Assume that the marble is made of pure glass, which has a known density of 2.5 g/mL.)

III. Volume of a Test Tube

volume measurements, in ascending order:

volume, mL   ____   ____   ____   ____   ____   ____   ____   ____   ____
            smallest   largest

median volume, mL   _____

mean volume, mL   _____

average deviation, mL   _____

standard deviation, mL   _____

IV. Temperature of Boiling Water

temperature measurements, in ascending order:

temperature, °C   ____   ____   ____   ____   ____   ____   ____   ____
            smallest   largest

median temperature, °C   _____

mean temperature, °C   _____

average deviation, °C   _____

standard deviation, °C   _____

average error, °C   _____

(The known boiling point of water at 1 atm pressure is 100.0 °C.)

Name   Section   Date

Interpretation of Your Results

Use the spaces provided for the answers and additional paper if necessary.

1. Why weren't you asked to calculate the average error in your measurements of the circumferences of the 150-mL beakers?

2. Suppose you randomly choose a 150-mL beaker and measure its circumference, using a piece of string.

(a) What measurement would you expect to obtain? Justify your answer.

(b) Comment on the precision and accuracy of your answer to (a).

3. Compare the standard deviation for your marble mass measurements with that for your marble density measurements. Explain any differences or similarities.

4. Compare the median and mean for your marble mass measurements. Explain any differences or similarities.

5. Are the marbles you measured in this experiment made of pure glass? Justify your answer.

6. Identify at least two possible sources of systematic error in your volume measurements of the test tubes.

7. Consider your set of temperature measurements of boiling water.

   (a) How precise are your measurements?

   (b) How accurate are your measurements?

_____   _____   _____
Name   Section   Date

Pre-Laboratory Assignment

1. Describe any precautions you should take when setting up your boiling water apparatus.

2. How would you expect the mean and the median to compare for very large numbers of measurements?

3. In a certain grocery store, the cost of 1 pound of hamburger on the last day of the month, for 6 successive months, was \$1.33, \$1.27, \$1.22, \$1.28, \$1.30, and \$1.31, respectively. Determine the mean and the median for the price of hamburger during this time period.

4. Seven students measured the volume of a flask with a neck mark indicating a fill volume of exactly 50.00 mL. To do so, each student filled the flask to the mark with water, then poured the water into a dry 100-mL graduated cylinder. Each student noted that there appeared to be some water droplets left in the flask after the water was poured out. The students read the volume of water in the cylinder. Their volume measurements are shown below.

	Student						
	1	*2*	*3*	*4*	*5*	*6*	*7*
volume, mL	49.5	48.7	47.2	49.1	49.2	48.3	49.3

(a) Calculate the mean, average error, average deviation, and standard deviation for these measurements.

(b) How accurate were the students' measurements? Identify the principal source of systematic error.

(c) How precise were the students' measurements? Identify possible sources of random error.

Density of Liquids and Solids

Prepared by H. A. Neidig, Lebanon Valley College, and
J. N. Spencer, Franklin and Marshall College

PURPOSE OF THE EXPERIMENT

Determine the density of an unknown sample of rubbing alcohol, a rubber stopper, and an unknown metal, using mass and volume measurements.

BACKGROUND INFORMATION

One of the physical properties of matter is **density**. This property is dependent on the volume and the mass of a sample of matter. The relationship between density, volume, and mass is shown in Equation 1.

$$\text{density} = \frac{\text{mass}}{\text{volume}}, \text{ or } d - \frac{m}{V} \qquad \text{(Eq. 1)}$$

The density of a liquid or of a solution is usually reported in units of grams per milliliter ($g\ mL^{-1}$). The density of a solid is reported in units of grams per cubic centimeter ($g\ cm^{-3}$). Because 1 mL is equivalent to 1 cm^3, these units are interchangeable.

The experimental procedure for obtaining laboratory data in order to calculate the density of an unknown sample of rubbing alcohol involves two steps. One step is to measure the mass of the sample. The second step is to measure its volume.

The mass of a sample of a substance is measured using a balance. If the substance is a liquid, the volume of the sample can be measured using a piece of calibrated glassware. For solid substances, the volume can be found by measuring the volume of liquid displaced by the sample. If the solid has a regular shape, such as a cube, its volume can be calculated using Equation 2. For other geometric shapes, appropriate equations are used to calculate their volumes.

$$
\begin{aligned}
\text{volume} &= \text{length} \times \text{width} \times \text{thickness}\\
&= \text{cm} \times \text{cm} \times \text{cm}\\
&= cm^3 = mL
\end{aligned}
\qquad \text{(Eq. 2)}
$$

When measuring volume by displacement, begin by pouring a liquid, such as water, into a graduated cylinder. Measure and record the volume of water. Add the weighed sample of the solid to the water in the cylinder. Measure the combined volume of water and the submerged solid. The difference between these two volumes is the volume of the solid.

In this experiment, you will use the experimentally determined mass and volume of the sample to calculate the density of the substance.

PROCEDURE

CAUTION

Wear departmentally approved eye protection while doing this experiment.

I. Determining the Density of an Unknown Rubbing Alcohol Solution

NOTE: Your laboratory instructor will give you directions for using your balance and will inform you as to the number of significant digits to the right of the decimal point to use when recording your data.

NOTE: The following instructions pertain to a top-loading balance.

1. Turn the balance on by pressing the control bar. The display should show zero grams. If it does not, consult your laboratory instructor.

2. Use crucible tongs to place a container or a piece of weighing paper on the center of the balance pan.

3. Press the control bar or the tare bar to display the container mass. Press the tare bar to return the balance display to zero.

    The mass of the container subtracted from the total mass of the container and its contents is called the **tare**. The tare function on your balance resets the display to zero grams with the empty container on the pan. The mass of the container is retained in the memory of the balance. This amount will be subtracted when the container and contents are weighed, to display only the mass of the contents.

4. Use tongs to remove the container from the balance. Place the substance or object to be weighed in the container.

5. Use tongs to replace the container and its contents on the center of the balance pan. The mass of the substance or object alone will appear on the display.

6. Read the mass of the substance or object, using the number of significant digits to the right of the decimal point specified by your laboratory instructor.

7. Use tongs to remove the container and its contents from the balance pan.

8. Place the balance in the rest position.

NOTE: The following instructions pertain to a centigram balance. If your centigram balance has an arrest lever, your laboratory instructor will give you additional directions regarding its use.

1. With all three sliding masses set to zero, check the balance to see whether the pointer freely swings an equal distance on either side of the zero mark. If it does not, consult your laboratory instructor.

2. Use crucible tongs to place the container on the center of the balance pan. The pointer on the center beam will deflect upward.

3. Move the appropriate sliding masses on the beams to balance the mass of the container. See **TECH 0382, Transfer and Measurement of Chemicals**, in this series, for additional information on the use of a centigram balance.

4. Read the positions of the masses on the beams. Calculate the mass of the container, using the number of significant digits to the right of the decimal point specified by your laboratory instructor.

5. Use tongs to remove the container from the balance pan. Add the substance or object to be weighed.

6. Use tongs to replace the container and its contents on the center of the balance pan.

7. Move the appropriate sliding masses on the beams to balance the mass of the container and its contents.

8. Read the positions of the masses on the beams. Calculate the combined mass of the container and its contents.

9. Return the sliding masses to their zero positions on the beams.

10. Use tongs to remove the container and its contents from the pan.

NOTE: The numbers appearing in parentheses indicate the lines on your Data Sheet on which data should be entered.

---

1. Weigh a clean, dry, 10-mL graduated cylinder. Record this mass on your Data Sheet (3).

CAUTION

Isopropyl alcohol is flammable and toxic if ingested. Keep isopropyl alcohol away from open flame and heat sources.

2. Use crucible tongs to remove the graduated cylinder from the balance. Obtain from your laboratory instructor a bottle containing your unknown rubbing alcohol solution. Record the code number of your unknown on your Data Sheet (1).

3. Pour 5 to 6 mL of rubbing alcohol solution from the bottle into the graduated cylinder. This amount of alcohol is Sample #1.

NOTE: The following instructions pertain to reading a volume in a graduated cylinder.

1. Place a piece of white paper or card directly behind the cylinder at the meniscus. See Figure 1.

2. Position your head so that your eye is at the same height as the level of the liquid. If you are holding the glassware, be sure that the glassware is exactly vertical.

3. Look straight at the meniscus through the glassware so that you see only a concave line, not a concave surface.

4. Read the level of the liquid at the bottom of the meniscus, the curved surface of the liquid. See Figure 2.

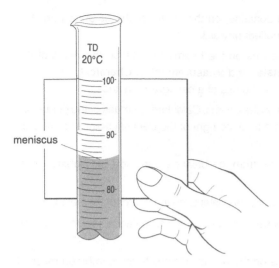

Figure 1
Finding the meniscus

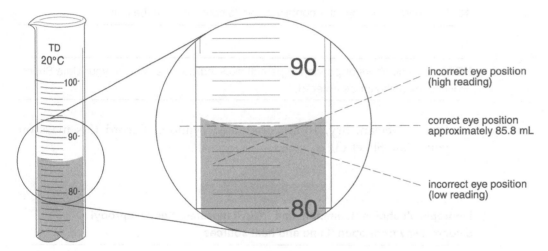

Figure 2
Using line of sight to read a meniscus

4. Read the volume of Sample #1 in the cylinder to the nearest one-tenth of a milliliter, 0.1 mL. Record this volume on your Data Sheet (4).

5. Weigh Sample #1 and the graduated cylinder, using the number of significant digits to the right of the decimal point specified by your laboratory instructor. Record this combined mass on your Data Sheet (2). If you are using a top-loading balance, you will not record the combined mass but will record only the mass of Sample #1 on your Data Sheet (7).

6. Transfer the alcohol sample to a test tube.

NOTE: In Steps 7–10, you will do a determination of the volume and mass of a second sample of the alcohol solution, using Sample #2.

---

7. Pour 4 to 5 mL of alcohol solution from the test tube into the graduated cylinder. This amount of alcohol solution is Sample #2.

8. Read the volume of Sample #2 in the graduated cylinder to the nearest 0.1 mL. Record this volume on your Data Sheet (6).

9. Weigh Sample #2 and the graduated cylinder, using the number of significant digits to the right of the decimal point specified by your laboratory instructor. Record this combined mass on your Data Sheet (5). If you are using a top-loading balance, you will not record the combined mass but will record only the mass of Sample #2 on your Data Sheet (9).

10. Pour Sample #2 and the alcohol solution remaining in the test tube into the container specified by your laboratory instructor and labeled, "Discarded Unknown Rubbing Alcohol Solutions."

II. Determining the Density of a Rubber Stopper

11. Obtain a rubber stopper from your laboratory instructor and record its identifying number on your Data Sheet (12).

CAUTION

Use crucible tongs to handle the rubber stopper.

12. Weigh the rubber stopper, using the number of significant digits to the right of the decimal point specified by your laboratory instructor. Record this mass on your Data Sheet (13).

13. Add approximately 50 to 60 mL of water to your 100-mL graduated cylinder. Read the volume of liquid in the cylinder to the nearest milliliter. Record this volume on your Data Sheet (14).

14. Slightly tilt the graduated cylinder and carefully slide the rubber stopper down the inside surface of the cylinder. Avoid splashing any of the water out of the cylinder.

15. Read the volume of liquid in the graduated cylinder to the nearest milliliter. Record this volume on your Data Sheet (15).

16. Drain the water from the graduated cylinder. Dry the stopper. Return the stopper to your laboratory instructor.

III. Determining the Density of an Unknown Metal

17. Obtain an unknown metal sample from your laboratory instructor and record its identifying number on your Data Sheet (18).

CAUTION

Use crucible tongs to handle the metal sample.

18. Wipe the sample carefully with a dampened cloth, dry thoroughly, and weigh. Record the mass on your Data Sheet (19).

19. Add 50 to 60 mL of water to your 100-mL graduated cylinder. Read the volume of liquid in the graduated cylinder to the nearest milliliter. Record this volume on your Data Sheet (20).

20. Slightly tilt the graduated cylinder and carefully slide the metal sample down the inside surface of the cylinder. Avoid splashing any of the water out of the cylinder.

21. Read the volume of the liquid in the graduated cylinder to the nearest milliliter. Record this volume on your Data Sheet (21).

22. Drain the water from the graduated cylinder. Dry the metal sample. Return the sample to your laboratory instructor.

CALCULATIONS

Do the following calculations and record the results on your Data Sheet.

I. Determining the Density of an Unknown Rubbing Alcohol Solution

NOTE: If you used a top-loading balance for this experiment, you will not need to do Steps 1 and 3.

1. Calculate the mass of Sample #1. Subtract the mass of the graduated cylinder (3) from the mass of the graduated cylinder and Sample #1 (2). Record this mass on your Data Sheet (7).

2. Calculate the density of Sample #1. Divide the mass of Sample #1 (7) by the volume of Sample #1 (4). Record the density of Sample #1 on your Data Sheet (8).

3. Calculate the mass of Sample #2. Subtract the mass of the graduated cylinder (3) from the mass of the graduated cylinder and Sample #2 (5). Record this mass on your Data Sheet (9).

4. Calculate the density of Sample #2. Divide the mass of Sample #2 (9) by the volume of Sample #2 (6). Record the density of Sample #2 on your Data Sheet (10).

5. Calculate the mean density of your unknown rubbing alcohol solution. Add the density of Sample #1 (8) and of Sample #2 (10), and divide by two. Record this mean density on your Data Sheet (11).

II. Determining the Density of a Rubber Stopper

6. Calculate the volume of the rubber stopper. Subtract the volume of the water (14) from the volume of the water and stopper (15). Record the volume of the stopper on your Data Sheet (16).

7. Calculate the density of the rubber stopper. Divide the mass of the rubber stopper (13) by the volume of the rubber stopper (16). Record this density on your Data Sheet (17).

III. Determining the Density of an Unknown Metal

8. Calculate the volume of the metal sample. Subtract the volume of the water (20) from the volume of the water and metal sample (21). Record the volume of the unknown metal on your Data Sheet (22).

9. Calculate the density of the unknown metal. Divide the mass of the unknown metal (19) by the volume of the metal (22). Record the density on your Data Sheet (23).

10. Identify the unknown metal. Use the list of metals and their densities supplied by your laboratory instructor to determine the identity of your unknown metal. Record its identity on your Data Sheet (24).

_____   _____   _____

Post-Laboratory Questions

(Use the spaces provided for the answers and additional paper if necessary.)

1. The density of ice at $0\,^\circ C$ is 0.9168 g mL^{-1}, and that of liquid water at $0\,^\circ C$ is 0.9999 g mL^{-1}.

    (1) What are the volumes of 1.000 g of ice and of 1.000 g of water at $0\,^\circ C$?

    (2) A sealed glass container with a capacity of exactly 100 mL contains 96.0 mL of liquid water at $0\,^\circ C$. If the water freezes, will the container rupture?

2. The volume of the nucleus of a carbon atom is about 9.9×10^{-39} mL. The molar mass of carbon is 12.00 g mol^{-1}. What is the density of the carbon nucleus?

3. Liquid mercury has a density of 13.6 g mL^{-1}. Which of the following substances will float on mercury, and which will sink?

	density, g mL^{-1}
neptunium	20.4
nickel	8.9
osmium	22.6
zinc	7.1
lead	11.4

4. A perfect cube of aluminum metal was found to weigh 20.00 g. The density of aluminum is 2.70 g mL^{-1}. What are the dimensions of the cube?

Name

Section

Date

Data Sheet

I. Determining the Density of an Unknown Rubbing Alcohol Solution

(1) code number of alcohol solution _____

(2) mass of Sample #1 and graduated cylinder, g _____

(3) mass of graduated cylinder, g _____

(4) volume of Sample #1, mL _____

(5) mass of Sample #2 and graduated cylinder, g _____

(6) volume of Sample #2, mL _____

(7) mass of Sample #1, g _____

(8) density of Sample #1, g mL^{-1} _____

(9) mass of Sample #2, g _____

(10) density of Sample #2, g mL^{-1} _____

(11) mean density of the unknown rubbing alcohol solution, g mL^{-1} _____

II. Determining the Density of a Rubber Stopper

(12) identifying number of rubber stopper _____

(13) mass of rubber stopper, g _____

(14) volume of water in graduated cylinder, mL _____

(15) volume of water and rubber stopper in graduated cylinder, mL _____

(16) volume of rubber stopper, mL _____

(17) density of the rubber stopper, g mL^{-1} _____

III. Determining the Density of an Unknown Metal

(18) identifying number of unknown metal   _____

(19) mass of metal, g   _____

(20) volume of water in graduated cylinder, mL   _____

(21) volume of water and metal in graduated cylinder, mL   _____

(22) volume of metal, mL   _____

(23) density of unknown metal, g mL^{-1} _____

(24) identity of unknown metal   _____

Calculations   (Show all your work. Use additional paper if necessary.)

Name   Section   Date

Pre-Laboratory Assignment

1. At 25 °C, 10.0181 g of an unknown liquid was found to have a volume of 6.75 mL.

(1) Calculate the density of the liquid.

_____
answer

(2) Which of the following liquids was the unknown?

	density, $g \, mL^{-1}$ at 25 °C
water	0.9982
toluene	0.8669
chloroform	1.4832

_____
answer

(3) If the unknown liquid had been water, what would the volume have been?

(4) What mass would a 10.00-mL sample of each of the liquids in (2) have?

water _____
answer

toluene _____
answer

chloroform _____
answer

2. A stopper was found to have a mass of 5.06 g. When placed in a graduated cylinder containing 45.2 mL of water, the volume of stopper and water was found to be 49.4 mL. Calculate the density of the stopper.

_____

answer

3. A chemist was given four unidentified, water-insoluble cubes measuring $1 \times 1 \times 1$ cm and asked to arrange these substances in order of their increasing density. These cubes were labeled $A, B, C,$ and D. As a reference, the chemist was also given the following liquids, whose densities in $g\, mL^{-1}$ at 20 °C are given below.

water	0.9982	nitromethane	1.1371
toluene	0.8669	chloroform	1.4832

The chemist added one of the four substances to one of the liquids and observed whether the substance floated or sank. By repeating this procedure with the other substances and liquids, he was able to make a series of observations about the relative densities of the substances and the liquids. Use the following selected observations to arrange the four unknown substances in order of increasing density. Briefly defend your order.

(1) Substance A sank in chloroform.

(2) Substance B floated in water but sank in toluene.

(3) Substance C sank in water but floated in chloroform and nitromethane.

(4) Substance D sank in nitromethane but did not sink as rapidly as Substance A did in nitromethane.

_____   _____   _____   _____

least dense   _most dense_

Percent Water in a Hydrate

Prepared by H. A. Neidig, Lebanon Valley College, and
J. N. Spencer, Franklin and Marshall College

PURPOSE OF THE EXPERIMENT

Determine the percent water in a hydrate sample.

BACKGROUND INFORMATION

Many substances contain water molecules as a part of their crystal structure. We call such solids **hydrates**, and we call the bound water the **water of hydration**.

A hydrate has a definite number of water molecules bound to each anhydrous salt unit. The formula of the hydrate copper(II) sulfate pentahydrate is

$$CuSO_4 \cdot 5\,H_2O$$

The dot indicates that the molecules of water are attached to the ions in $CuSO_4$ by weak bonds.

Calcium sulfate occurs in nature as the mineral anhydrite ($CaSO_4$). It is also found as a dihydrate, gypsum, ($CaSO_4 \cdot 2\,H_2O$), in very large deposits. When gypsum is heated, the substance loses water, forming plaster of Paris $(CaSO_4)_2 \cdot \frac{1}{2}\,H_2O$, according to Equation 1.

$$CaSO_4 \cdot 2\,H_2O(s) \xrightarrow{\text{heat}} (CaSO_4)_2 \cdot {}^1/_2\,H_2O(s) + {}^3/_2\,H_2O(g) \qquad \text{(Eq. 1)}$$

When we mix finely ground plaster of Paris with water, small tightly fitting crystals of gypsum bond together. During the process, the material increases in volume and will fit tightly into any mold into which it is poured. Plaster of Paris has many uses; for example, it is a component of plaster for interior walls of buildings and of stucco and wallboard.

Gypsum ($CaSO_4 \cdot 2\,H_2O$) also is used in a wide variety of applications such as Portland cement, dental plasters, and blackboard chalk.

Anhydrous calcium sulfate ($CaSO_4$) is available commercially as Drierite and is used as a drying agent for removing water from organic liquids and a variety of gases.

We can drive off the water of hydration by heating the hydrate, as shown in Equation 2 on the next page. If blue $CuSO_4 \cdot 5\,H_2O$ is heated, the water of hydration is released as water vapor, and solid white anhydrous $CuSO_4$ remains.

$$CuSO_4 \cdot 5\,H_2O(s) \xrightarrow{\text{heat}} CuSO_4(s) \;+\; 5\,H_2O(g) \qquad (\text{Eq. 2})$$
$$\underset{\text{hydrated salt}}{} \qquad\qquad \underset{\text{anhydrous salt}}{} \quad \underset{\text{water vapor}}{}$$

The reverse reaction of Equation 2 may also occur. Anhydrous $CuSO_4$ is white, but upon exposure to air, the anhydrous salt absorbs water. This reaction produces blue $CuSO_4 \cdot 5\,H_2O$.

In some cases, compounds can actually dissolve in their water of hydration. Salts such as calcium chloride ($CaCl_2$), magnesium sulfate ($MgSO_4$), $CuSO_4$, and $CaSO_4$, can absorb so much water that they form solutions. These salts are said to be **deliquescent**. We often use anhydrous salts of this type as drying agents.

Some hydrated salts such as $Na_2SO_4 \cdot 10\,H_2O$ tend to lose water under normal conditions of temperature and pressure. Such salts are said to be **efflorescent**.

In this experiment, you will determine the mass of the hydrated salt before and after heating. The loss in mass of the hydrated salt is equal to the mass of water in the salt. From these data, you will calculate the percent by mass of water in a hydrated salt.

PROCEDURE

CHEMICAL ALERT

unknown hydrate—irritant

CAUTION

Wear departmentally approved eye protection while doing this experiment.

NOTE: Throughout the procedure, use crucible tongs to handle the crucible and its cover.

NOTE: The numbers appearing in parentheses indicate the lines on your Data Sheet on which that data should be entered.

1. Obtain a sample of a hydrate from your laboratory instructor.
   Record the number of your sample on your Data Sheet (1).

NOTE: If the crucible or cover are not clean, their combined mass may change during the heating in Steps 9–10. If this happens, your results will be erroneous. Ask your laboratory instructor for a clean, dry crucible and cover or for instructions on cleaning your crucible and cover.

2. Use crucible tongs to place a clean, dry porcelain crucible on the balance pan.

NOTE: Your laboratory instructor will give you specific directions for using your balance and will instruct you on the number of significant digits to the right of the decimal point to use when recording your data.

3. Weigh the crucible without its cover and record the mass of the crucible on your Data Sheet (3).

4. Use crucible tongs to remove the crucible from the balance. Use a spatula to transfer about 2 g of the hydrate to the crucible.
   Place the crucible and its contents on the balance.

5. Determine the mass of the crucible and hydrate to the number of significant digits specified by your laboratory instructor.
   Record this mass on your Data Sheet (2).

6. Place an iron ring on a support stand. Allow sufficient height to place a Bunsen burner beneath the ring, as shown in Figure 1.

7. Place a Nichrome or clay triangle on the ring. Use crucible tongs to place the crucible and sample at a slight angle on the triangle, as shown in Figure 1.

8. Use crucible tongs to place a crucible cover on the open crucible so that the cover is slightly ajar, as shown in Figure 2 on the next page. If the entire opening of the crucible is covered, the water vapor released by heating cannot escape.

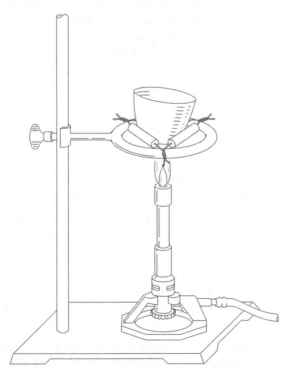

Figure 1
Heating a hydrate in a crucible

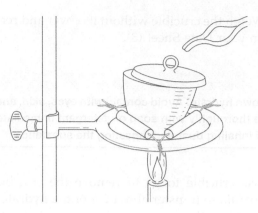

Figure 2
Position of a crucible cover for heating

NOTE: Your laboratory instructor will describe and demonstrate the Bunsen burner adjustments used to obtain a nonluminous flame in Step 9.

---

9. Turn on the gas cock and light the gas escaping from the Bunsen burner. Adjust the air and gas to obtain a nonluminous flame.

CAUTION

⚠

Do not touch the hot barrel of the Bunsen burner, the iron ring, the triangle, or the support stand. Be careful when removing the hot crucible and cover from the triangle. If the hot crucible cover falls, do not touch it with your hands. If the triangle adheres to the hot crucible, transfer the triangle and the crucible to the ceramic-centered wire gauze on the bench. After cooling, you should be able to remove the crucible from the triangle.

NOTE: Your laboratory instructor will describe and demonstrate how to heat the crucible, cover, and its contents gently in Step 10 and strongly in Step 12.

---

10. Gently heat the crucible for 5 min by slowly moving the Bunsen burner flame back and forth across the bottom of the crucible.

11. Place the lighted burner on the base of the support stand under the crucible so that the flame contacts the lower edge of the bottom of the crucible.

12. Heat the crucible more strongly until the bottom of the crucible is slightly red. Continue heating for another 10 min.

13. Turn off the gas cock to extinguish the Bunsen burner flame. Allow the crucible to cool for 5 to 10 min.

14. Use crucible tongs to remove the cover from the crucible and place it on the wire gauze on the bench to cool. Then, use the crucible tongs to remove the crucible and contents from the triangle and place them on the wire gauze to cool.

> **CAUTION**
>
> **Do not place a hot object on the balance pan. The mass of any object cannot be determined accurately unless the object is at the same temperature as the balance.**

15. When no heat is felt when you hold your hand 1 to 2 cm from the crucible, use your crucible tongs to transfer the crucible to your balance. Weigh the cooled crucible and its contents to the number of significant digits specified by your laboratory instructor.

    Record the mass of the crucible and its contents on your Data Sheet (5).

16. Discard the contents of your crucible as directed by your laboratory instructor.

17. Thoroughly wash your crucible and crucible cover with tap water. Rinse them with distilled or deionized water, and dry them with a disposable towel.

18. If time permits, do a second determination. Use a second portion of your sample and repeat Steps 2–17, using a clean, dry crucible and crucible cover.

> **CAUTION**
>
> **Wash your hands thoroughly with soap or detergent before leaving the laboratory.**

CALCULATIONS

(Do the following calculations for each determination and record the results on your Data Sheet. The numbers in parentheses refer to the numbered lines on your Data Sheet.)

1. Calculate the mass of the hydrate heated.

   Subtract the mass of the crucible (3) from the mass of the crucible and hydrate (2).

   Record the mass of the hydrate on your Data Sheet (4).

2. Calculate the mass of water lost from the hydrate during the heating.

   Subtract the mass of the crucible and anhydrous salt (5) from the mass of the crucible and hydrate (2).

   Record the mass of water lost on your Data Sheet (6).

3. Calculate the percent water in the hydrate

$$\frac{\text{percent}}{\text{water}} = \left(\frac{\text{mass of water lost, g (6)}}{\text{mass of hydrate, g (4)}}\right)(100\%)$$

   Record this percent on your Data Sheet (7).

4. If you did a second determination, calculate the mean percent water in the hydrate.

   Record the mean percent on your Data Sheet (8).

Post-Laboratory Questions

(Use the spaces provided for your answers and additional paper if necessary.)

1. A student performed the experiment in this module but failed to follow the procedure exactly, keeping the crucible completely covered during the entire heating and cooling processes.

   (1) Explain the probable effect of this procedural change on the experimental results.

   (2) Would the student's calculated percent water in the hydrate be high, low, or unaffected? Briefly explain.

2. A student was asked to identify an unknown hydrate by following the procedure described in this module. After heating and cooling, a 2.752-g sample of this unknown weighed 1.941 g. Students were given a list of possible compounds from which to identify their unknowns: $LiNO_3 \cdot 3\,H_2O$, $Ca(NO_3)_2 \cdot 4\,H_2O$, and $Sr(NO_3)_2 \cdot 4\,H_2O$.

   (1) Calculate percent water in the student's unknown.

(2) Could the unknown possibly have been $Sr(NO_3)_2 \cdot 4\,H_2O$? Briefly explain.

(3) What is the probable identity of the student's unknown?

(4) Based on the student's results and your answer to (3), what is the most probable source of error in the experiment?

_____   _____   _____
Name   *Section*   *Date*

Data Sheet

(1) sample number _____

	determinations	
	1	*2*
(2) mass of crucible and hydrate (before heating), g	_____	_____
(3) mass of crucible, g	_____	_____
(4) mass of hydrate, g	_____	_____
(5) mass of crucible and anhydrous salt (after final heating), g	_____	_____
(6) mass of water lost from hydrate, g	_____	_____
(7) percent water in hydrate, %	_____	_____
(8) mean percent water in the hydrate, %	_____	

Calculations   (Show all your work. Use additional paper if necessary.)

Name   _Section_   _Date_

Pre-Laboratory Assignment

1. Explain why it is necessary to be extremely careful when working with barium chloride dihydrate.

2. Chemists use symbolism to facilitate the writing of chemical equations. Using your textbook as a reference, if necessary, briefly explain the difference between

(1) $CuSO_4(s)$ and $CuSO_4 \cdot 5 H_2O(s)$

(2) $CuSO_4(s)$ and $CuSO_4(aq)$

(3) $CuSO_4 \cdot 5 H_2O(s)$ and $CuSO_4(aq)$

3. The mass of a crucible and a hydrated salt was found to be 21.447 g. The mass of the crucible and the anhydrous salt was 20.070 g. The mass of the crucible was 17.985 g.

(1) Calculate the mass of the hydrate heated.

(2) Calculate the mass of water lost from the hydrate during heating.

(3) Calculate the percent water in the hydrate.

Naming Inorganic Chemical Substances

Prepared by M. L. Gillette, Indiana University Kokomo, and
H. A. Neidig, Lebanon Valley College

PURPOSE OF THE EXERCISE

Use a universal systematic method for naming inorganic chemical substances. Derive substance names from chemical formulas, and chemical formulas from substance names.

BACKGROUND REQUIRED

You should be familiar with the names and chemical symbols of the elements, and the relative positions of metals and nonmetals in the periodic table. You should also know how to interpret a chemical formula.

BACKGROUND INFORMATION

It is vital that people around the world use a common language when referring to any of the seemingly infinite number of chemical substances that exist. The universal **nomenclature** system currently in use is based on the identity and number of atoms making up one unit of the substance. To clarify what may initially seem like a confusing system, we will outline the process of naming an inorganic substance, using a flowchart. This will help us focus on the characteristics of the substance's formula, hence, those of its name. The flowchart we will use is shown in Figure 1 on the next page.

Following the Flowchart

I. Distinguishing between Elements and Compounds

If the chemical formula for a substance includes only one kind of atom, we say that the substance is an **element**, or that it is in **elemental form**. Sometimes, the elemental form of a substance includes multiple identical atoms joined together, such as O_2 (elemental oxygen). If this is the case, the substance's chemical formula will reflect this fact. However, if the substance's formula includes two or more different elements, we say that the substance is a **compound**.

Illustration: Na, Cl_2, and S_8 are elements; H_2O and Na_2CrO_4 are compounds.

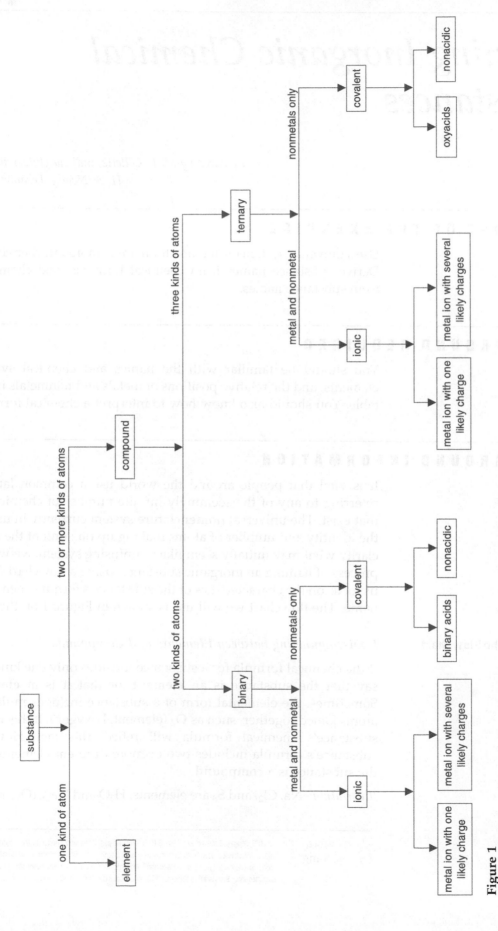

Figure 1
Flowchart outlining the procedure used for naming inorganic chemical substances

II. Naming Elements

If the substance is in elemental form, we give it the name of the elemental symbol in the substance's formula, regardless of how many atoms are in the elemental unit.

Illustration: Na is sodium, Cl_2 is chlorine, and S_8 is sulfur.

III. Distinguishing between Binary and Ternary Compounds

Most compounds fall into either of two categories, binary or ternary. The formulas of **binary** compounds include two different kinds of atoms. The formulas of **ternary** compounds include three different kinds of atoms.

Illustration: NaCl is a binary compound; H_2CO_3 is a ternary compound.

IV. Distinguishing between Ionic and Covalent Compounds

Most compounds whose formulas include both metallic and nonmetallic atoms are **ionic**. Most compounds whose formulas include only non-metallic atoms are **covalent**. In the context of nomenclature and most chemical behavior, hydrogen is considered a nonmetal.

Illustration: NaCl is an ionic compound; H_2CO_3 is a covalent compound.

Ionic compounds contain one or more **cations** (positively charged ions) and one or more **anions** (negatively charged ions). Ions formed from single atoms are called **monoatomic** ions. Ions formed from two or more atoms are called **polyatomic** ions.

Illustration: Na^+ and Cl^- are monoatomic ions; CO_3^{2-} is a polyatomic ion.

Ionic compounds are electrically neutral. In each unit of the compound, the total positive charge contributed by the cation(s) is balanced by the total negative charge contributed by the anion(s).

The cations in ionic compounds are usually metal ions. Some metals form cations with only one likely charge, while others form cations with several likely charges, depending upon reaction conditions.

Figure 2 shows some commonly occurring monoatomic ions, including metals and nonmetals.

V. Naming Binary Compounds

In order to name a binary compound, we must first decide whether it is ionic or covalent.

A. Naming Ionic Binary Compounds If the compound is ionic, we must determine whether the metal component is one that forms cations with one or several likely charges. To do so, we refer to Figure 2 on the next page.

Compounds containing a metal that forms cations with only one likely charge: Name the metal ion first, using its elemental name, then the nonmetal ion, changing the ending of its name to "ide".

Illustration: Na_2S is sodium sulfide; CaO is calcium oxide.

Compounds containing a metal that forms cations with several likely charges: Name the metal ion first, using its elemental name. Immediately following

1	2											3	4	5	6	7	8
H^+																	
Li^+														N^{3-}	O^{2-} O^-	F^-	
Na^+	Mg^{2+}											Al^{3+}			S^{2-}	Cl^-	
K^+	Ca^{2+}		Ti^{2+} Ti^{4+}		Cr^{2+} Cr^{3+}	Mn^{2+}	Fe^{2+} Fe^{3+}	Co^{2+} Co^{3+}		Cu^+ Cu^{2+}	Zn^{2+}					Br^-	
Rb^+	Sr^{2+}									Ag^+	Cd^{2+}		Sn^{2+} Sn^{4+}			I^-	
Cs^+	Ba^{2+}																

Figure 2
Commonly occurring monoatomic ions, as positioned in the periodic table

the metal name, write the cation's charge in parentheses, using capital Roman numerals. You can determine the cation's charge by looking at the possible anion charge(s) and figuring out which combination of cation/anion charges results in an electrically neutral compound. Then name the nonmetal ion, changing the ending of its name to "ide".

The use of Roman numerals to indicate metal ion charges is called the **Stock system**. There are older systems for indicating metal ion charges, but we will not discuss them here.

Illustration: FeO is iron(II) oxide; Fe_2S_3 is iron(III) sulfide.

B. Naming Covalent Binary Compounds   *Covalent binary compounds:* Several covalent binary compounds are known only by their common, or familiar, names. For example, NH_3 is ammonia, and H_2O is water. For most other covalent binary compounds, begin by naming the first element in the formula. Then name the second element, changing the ending of its name to "ide".

Illustration: IBr is iodine bromide.

In some instances, two or more covalent binary compounds contain the same two elements in different ratios; for example, CO and CO_2. When naming these types of compounds, we indicate the number of each component present in the formula, using the prefixes shown in Table 1. For simplicity's sake, we do not use the prefix mono with the first element in a compound name.

Illustration: CO is carbon monoxide (*not* monocarbon monoxide); CO_2 is carbon dioxide; N_2O is dinitrogen monoxide.

Some covalent binary compounds containing hydrogen are **acidic**, which means that they release hydrogen ions in aqueous solutions. When dissolved in water, these compounds are called **binary acids**. When they are not dissolved in water, these compounds are named using the method described above. Hence, HCl(g) is hydrogen chloride, and H_2S(g) is hydrogen sulfide (*not* dihydrogen monosulfide because only one H–S combination exists).

Table 1 *Prefixes used to indicate the number of atoms in the formula of a chemical compound*

number	prefix	number	prefix
1	mono	4	tetra
2	di	5	penta
3	tri	6	hexa

Table 2 *Chemical formulas and names of some binary acids*

chemical formula	name
HF (aq)	hydrofluoric acid
HCl (aq)	hydrochloric acid
HBr (aq)	hydrobromic acid
HI (aq)	hydroiodic acid
H_2S (aq)	hydrosulfuric acid

Binary acids: Covalent binary compounds that release hydrogen ions when dissolved in water are named as shown in Table 2.

VI. Naming Ternary Compounds

In order to name a ternary compound, we must first determine whether it is ionic or covalent.

A. Naming Ionic Ternary Compounds   Many ionic ternary compounds contain one or more polyatomic ions. Table 3 lists some common polyatomic ions. These ions can combine with metals that form ions with only one likely charge or several likely charges.

Table 3 *Names and chemical formulas for some common polyatomic ions*

name	chemical formula	name	chemical formula
acetate	$C_2H_3O_2^-$	hydrogen sulfite (bisulfite)	HSO_3^-
ammonium	NH_4^+	hydroxide	OH^-
carbonate	CO_3^{2-}	hypochlorite*	ClO^-
chlorate*	ClO_3^-	nitrate	NO_3^-
chlorite*	ClO_2^-	nitrite	NO_2^-
chromate	CrO_4^{2-}	oxalate	$C_2O_4^{2-}$
cyanide	CN^-	perchlorate*	ClO_4^-
dichromate	$Cr_2O_7^{2-}$	permanganate	MnO_4^-
dihydrogen phosphate	$H_2PO_4^-$	phosphate	PO_4^{3-}
hydrogen carbonate (bicarbonate)	HCO_3^-	sulfate	SO_4^{2-}
hydrogen phosphate	HPO_4^{2-}	sulfite	SO_3^{2-}
hydrogen sulfate	HSO_4^-		

*Bromine (Br) and iodine (I) form analogous anions, which are named accordingly.

Compounds containing a metal that forms cations with only one likely charge: Name the cation first, then the anion. If the anion is monoatomic, name it using its elemental name, changing the ending to "ide". If the cation or anion is polyatomic, use the name from Table 3.

Illustration: NH_4Cl is ammonium chloride; $NaClO_3$ is sodium chlorate.

Compounds containing a metal that forms cations with several likely charges: Name the metal first, using its elemental name. Then write the metal ion's charge in parentheses, using capital Roman numerals. Then name the anion. If the anion is polyatomic, use the name from Table 3.

Illustration: $CuCO_3$ is copper(II) carbonate; $Fe(NO_3)_3$ is iron(III) nitrate.

B. Naming Oxyacids, Covalent Ternary Compounds Containing Oxyanions All but two of the anions in Table 3 contain oxygen. We refer to these oxygen-containing anions as **oxyanions**. When hydrogen atom(s) replace the metal ion(s) in an ionic ternary compound containing an oxyanion, the result is a covalent ternary compound that we call an **oxyacid**. For example, H can replace Na in $NaClO_3$, resulting in $HClO_3$, an oxyacid. When dissolved in water, oxyacids release hydrogen ions to the solution. The best way to learn to distinguish oxyacids from other covalent ternary compounds is to become familiar with the oxyanions in Table 3.

Oxyacids: Table 4 lists some of the oxyanions from Table 3, along with the oxyacids containing those anions.

Note that some of the oxyanions listed in Tables 3 and 4 contain the same nonmetal atom combined with different numbers of oxygen atoms. For example, nitrogen (N) is present in both NO_2^- and NO_3^-; sulfur (S) in SO_3^{2-} and SO_4^{2-}; and chlorine (Cl) in ClO^-, ClO_2^-, ClO_3^-, and ClO_4^-. We distinguish among such compounds using the following scheme.

When the same nonmetal is present in two different oxyanions, we name the oxyanions and related oxyacids as follows. We give the oxyanion with fewer oxygen atoms the nonmetal name, changing the ending to "ite", and we give the related acid the name of the oxyanion, changing the ending to "ous". We give the oxyanion with more oxygen atoms the nonmetal name, changing the ending to "ate", and we give the related oxyacid the name of the oxyanion, changing the ending to "ic".

Table 4 *Some oxyanions and their related oxyacids*

chemical formula of oxyanion	oxyanion name	chemical formula of related oxyacid	oxyacid name
ClO^-*	hypochlorite	$HClO$*	hypochlorous acid
ClO_2^-*	chlorite	$HClO_2$*	chlorous acid
ClO_3^-*	chlorate	$HClO_3$*	chloric acid
ClO_4^-*	perchlorate	$HClO_4$*	perchloric acid
NO_2^-	nitrite	HNO_2	nitrous acid
NO_3^-	nitrate	HNO_3	nitric acid
SO_3^{2-}	sulfite	H_2SO_3	sulfurous acid
SO_4^{2-}	sulfate	H_2SO_4	sulfuric acid

*Bromine and iodine form analogous oxyanions and oxyacids, which are named accordingly.

Illustration: SO_3^{2-} is the sulf*ite* ion, and H_2SO_3 is sulfur*ous* acid; SO_4^{2-} is the sulf*ate* ion, and H_2SO_4 is sulfur*ic* acid.

When the same nonmetal is present in four different oxyanions, as is the case for chlorine, bromine, and iodine, we distinguish among the oxyanions and related oxyacids as follows. We give the oxyanion with four oxygen atoms the nonmetal name, adding the prefix "per" and changing the ending to "ate". We give the related oxyacid the oxyanion name, adding the prefix "per" and changing the ending to "ic". We give the oxyanion with three oxygen atoms the nonmetal name, changing the ending to "ate". We name the related oxyacid by changing the end of the oxyanion name to "ic". We name the oxyanion with two oxygen atoms by changing the end of the nonmetal name to "ite". We name the related oxyacid by changing the ending of the oxyanion name to "ous". Finally, we give the oxyanion with one oxygen atom the nonmetal name, adding the prefix "hypo" and changing the ending to "ite". We name the related oxyacid by adding the prefix "hypo" and changing the ending of the oxyanion name to "ous".

Illustration: ClO_4^- is the **perchlor***ate* ion, and $HClO_4$ is **perchlor***ic* acid; ClO_3^- is the chlor*ate* ion, and $HClO_3$ is chlor*ic* acid; ClO_2^- is the chlor*ite* ion, and $HClO_2$ is chlor*ous* acid; ClO^- is the **hypo**chlor*ite* ion, and $HClO$ is **hypo**chlor*ous* acid.

Example

Problem Name the compound $Al(ClO_4)_3$.

Solution *Follow the flowchart in Figure 1 from "substance" to the correct general classification for $Al(ClO_4)_3$, and then name the compound.*

(a) $Al(ClO_4)_3$ is composed of more than one kind of atom, so it is a compound.

(b) $Al(ClO_4)_3$ is composed of three kinds of atoms, so it is a ternary compound.

(c) $Al(ClO_4)_3$ is composed of a metal (Al) and a polyatomic anion containing nonmetals (ClO_4^-), so it is an ionic ternary compound.

(d) Aluminum ions occur only as Al^{3+}, so we give the cation its elemental name, aluminum. As listed in Table 4, ClO_4^- is the perchlorate ion. Therefore, the name of $Al(ClO_4)_3$ is aluminum perchlorate.

In This Exercise

You will classify and name various substances, based on their chemical formulas. You will classify and write chemical formulas for other substances, based on their names. You will review a list of chemical formulas and related names, and correct the names so they are appropriate for the related formulas. Finally, you will review a list of compound names and related chemical formulas, and correct the formulas.

Name   Partner   Section   Date

Exercises

1. Classify the following substances, using the procedure outlined by the flowchart in Figure 1. For example: HCl is a covalent binary compound; NaI is an ionic binary compound with only one likely charge on the cation.

(a) SO_2 _____

(b) I_2 _____

(c) H_2SO_4 _____

(d) K_2SO_4 _____

(e) $CuCrO_4$ _____

(f) $Co_2(CrO_4)_3$ _____

2. Name the substances you classified in 1.

(a) _____

(b) _____

(c) _____

(d) _____

(e) _____

(f) _____

3. Classify and name the following substances.

chemical formula	classification	name
(a) P_4		
(b) LiBr		
(c) $SnCl_2$		
(d) K_2SO_3		
(e) $Fe(ClO_3)_2$		
(f) CS_2		
(g) $Sr(OH)_2$		
(h) N_2O_4		
(i) $Al(NO_3)_3$		
(j) NO		
(k) $NaIO_3$		
(l) $HBrO_3$		
(m) $KMnO_4$		
(n) $Ti(CO_3)_2$		

4. Classify and write the chemical formulas for the following substances.

name	chemical formula	classification
(a) hypobromous acid		
(b) phosphorus pentachloride		
(c) sodium oxalate		
(d) calcium iodide		
(e) hydrobromic acid		
(f) dinitrogen pentaoxide		
(g) silver sulfide		
(h) iodous acid		
(i) iron(III) phosphate		
(j) cobalt		
(k) titanium(II) nitrate		
(l) calcium phosphate		
(m) manganese perchlorate		
(n) sodium sulfite		
(o) tetraphosphorus trisulfide		

5. The chemical name given to each of the compounds below is incorrect. Write the correct name for each compound, and briefly explain the basis of your correction.

compound	incorrect name	correct name	explanation
(a) $SnCl_4$	tin chloride		
(b) SF_6	monosulfur hexafluoride		
(c) AlF_3	aluminum(III) fluoride		
(d) HIO_4	iodic acid		
(e) F_2	difluorine		

6. The formula given for each of the chemical names below is incorrect. Write the correct chemical formula for each compound, and briefly explain the basis of your correction.

name	incorrect chemical formula	correct chemical formula	explanation
(a) copper(II) carbonate	Cu_2CO_3		
(b) potassium periodate	KIO_3		
(c) carbon tetrachloride	CCl_3		
(d) strontium sulfate	$SrSO_3$		
(e) barium nitrite	$BaNO_2$		

Titrating the Acetic Acid in Vinegar

*Prepared by M. L. Gillette, Indiana University Kokomo, H. A. Neidig, Lebanon Valley College, and
J. N. Spencer, Franklin and Marshall College*

PURPOSE OF THE EXPERIMENT

Determine the molar concentration of acetic acid in vinegar by titrating it with a standard sodium hydroxide solution.

BACKGROUND REQUIRED

You should understand the concepts associated with stoichiometry and acid–base chemistry.

BACKGROUND INFORMATION

Vinegar, a familiar ingredient in foods, is an aqueous (water) solution of acetic acid ($HC_2H_3O_2$, which we will symbolize as HOAc), often with added flavorings. Acetic acid can be neutralized by sodium hydroxide (NaOH) solution, as shown in Equation 1.

$$\underset{acid}{HOAc(aq)} + \underset{base}{NaOH(aq)} \rightarrow \underset{salt}{NaOAc(aq)} + \underset{water}{H_2O(\ell)} \qquad \text{(Eq. 1)}$$

We can determine the exact HOAc concentration in a vinegar sample by titrating a measured volume of the vinegar with a **standard** NaOH solution, one of known concentration. A **titration** is the measurement of the volume of standard solution required to completely react with a measured volume or mass of the substance being analyzed. When performing a titration, we often add a third substance, called an **indicator,** which changes color when the titration is complete. The titration **end point** is signaled by this color change. For convenience, we will express HOAc concentration in terms of **molarity (*M*)**, the number of moles of solute per liter of solution.

Phenolphthalein is a good indicator for this titration. Phenolphthalein is colorless in acidic solution and pink in basic solution. As soon as any excess NaOH is added to the titration mixture, the phenolphthalein turns pink, signaling the end point of the titration.

Example   **Problem** Find the molarity of HOAc in a vinegar sample when 22.34 mL of
                             0.4916M NaOH are required to neutralize 20.00 mL of vinegar.

                    Solution **(1)** *Calculate the number of moles of NaOH required to neutralize the*
                             HOAc.

$$\begin{array}{l}\text{number of moles of} \\ \text{NaOH required, mol}\end{array} = \left(\begin{array}{l}\text{volume of NaOH} \\ \text{solution used, mL}\end{array}\right)\left(\frac{1\,\text{L}}{1000\,\text{mL}}\right)\left(\begin{array}{l}\text{concentration of} \\ \text{NaOH solution, mol/L}\end{array}\right) \quad \text{(Eq. 2)}$$

$$= (22.34\ \text{mL})\left(\frac{1\,\text{L}}{1000\,\text{mL}}\right)(0.4916\ \text{mol/L})$$

$$= 1.098 \times 10^{-2}\ \text{mol NaOH}$$

(2) *Calculate the number of moles of HOAc present in the vinegar*
sample titrated.

$$\begin{array}{l}\text{number of moles of HOAc in} \\ \text{titrated vinegar sample, mol}\end{array} = \left(\begin{array}{l}\text{number of moles} \\ \text{of NaOH required, mol}\end{array}\right)\left(\frac{1\ \text{mol HOAc}}{1\ \text{mol NaOH}}\right) \quad \text{(Eq. 3)}$$

$$= 1.098 \times 10^{-2}\ \text{mol NaOH}\ \left(\frac{1\ \text{mol HOAc}}{1\ \text{mol NaOH}}\right)$$

$$= 1.098 \times 10^{-2}\ \text{mol HOAc}$$

(3) *Calculate the molarity of HOAc in the vinegar sample.*

$$\begin{array}{l}\text{molarity of HOAc in} \\ \text{vinegar sample, mol/L}\end{array} = \left(\frac{\text{number of moles of HOAc in vinegar sample, mol}}{\text{volume of vinegar sample analyzed, L}}\right) \quad \text{(Eq. 4)}$$

$$= \frac{1.098 \times 10^{-2}\ \text{mol HOAc}}{(20.00\ \text{mL})\left(\frac{1\,\text{L}}{1000\,\text{mL}}\right)}$$

$$= 0.5491\ \text{mol/L} = 0.5491M$$

In This Experiment   You will titrate the HOAc in a vinegar sample with standard NaOH
                             solution and then safely dispose of your discarded solutions. From your
                             titration data, you will calculate the molarity of HOAc in the vinegar.

PROCEDURE

CAUTION   ⚠

Wear departmentally approved safety goggles while doing this experiment.
    Always use caution in the laboratory. Many chemicals are potentially harmful.
Prevent contact with your eyes, skin, and clothing. Avoid ingesting any of the
reagents.

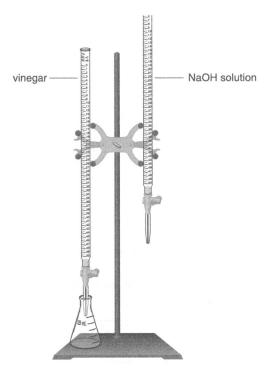

vinegar ———   ——— NaOH solution

Figure 1
A titration assembly

NOTE:

• The general set-up for this experiment is shown in Figure 1.

• Dispose of your reaction mixtures and rinses according to your laboratory instructor's directions.

• Record all of your data on your Data and Observations sheet.

I. Preparing the Vinegar Sample for Titration

1. Obtain about 125 mL of a vinegar sample in a dry 250-mL beaker. Record the identification code of your sample.
    Label a 400-mL beaker "Discarded Solutions".

2. Rinse the buret with vinegar solution. Collect the rinses in the Discarded Solutions beaker. Clamp the buret to the support stand. Label the buret "vinegar".

3. Fill the buret with vinegar solution to a level above the 0-mL calibration mark.

NOTE: Make sure that the buret tip is completely filled with vinegar solution. There should not be any air bubbles in the buret barrel or tip. This is because the volume of any such bubbles will be included in the volume of vinegar titrated, which will lead to an erroneously low concentration of HOAc in the vinegar.

---

4. If there are any air bubbles in the buret tip or barrel, eliminate them by opening the stopcock for 1–2 s. Then slowly drain vinegar solution into the Discarded Solutions beaker until the bottom of the meniscus is at, or slightly below, the 0-mL calibration. Touch the inner sidewall of the

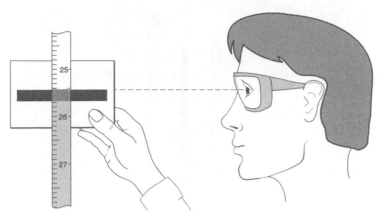

Figure 2
Reading the liquid level in a buret

beaker to the buret tip to remove any vinegar solution that may be clinging to the tip.

NOTE: A 50-mL buret is calibrated in units of 0.1 mL, but measurements to the nearest 0.01 mL can be reproducibly estimated. Record every reading to the nearest 0.01 mL.

When reading the buret, hold a white card marked with a dark stripe directly behind and slightly below the meniscus, as shown in Figure 2. Keep your line of sight level with the bottom of the meniscus.

5. Read the buret and estimate to the nearest 0.01 mL and record this initial vinegar buret reading in the column headed "determination 1".

6. Deliver 20–25 mL of your vinegar sample into a 125-mL Erlenmeyer flask. Record the final vinegar buret reading for determination 1.

7. Add 40 mL of distilled or deionized water and three drops of phenolphthalein solution to the vinegar in the flask. Gently swirl the flask to mix the solution.

II. Preparing the NaOH Buret

CAUTION

NaOH solution is toxic and corrosive, and it can cause skin burns.

---

8. Obtain about 150 mL of standard NaOH solution in a dry 250-mL Erlenmeyer flask. Stopper the flask with a clean cork, and keep the flask stoppered when not in use. Record the molarity of the NaOH solution to four significant figures.

9. Rinse a second 50-mL buret with standard NaOH solution. Collect the rinses in the Discarded Solutions beaker. Clamp the buret to the support stand. Label the buret "NaOH".

10. Fill this buret with NaOH solution to a level above the 0-mL calibration. Follow the procedure of Step 4 to fill and remove air bubbles from the buret tip.

   Read the buret and estimate to the nearest 0.01 mL and record this initial NaOH buret reading in the column headed "determination 1".

Figure 3
Positioning the NaOH buret for titration and manipulating the stopcock

11. Position the NaOH buret and the 125-mL Erlenmeyer flask containing the vinegar solution as shown in Figure 3.

III. Titrating Vinegar

NOTE: As the titration proceeds, you will observe a pink coloration at the point where NaOH solution contacts the surface of the vinegar solution. As you approach the end point, pink will begin to momentarily flash through the titration mixture and you should start adding the NaOH solution dropwise.

Stop the titration when pink persists throughout the titration mixture for 30 s after you have thoroughly swirled the flask.

---

12. Titrate the vinegar sample, adding 1–2 mL of NaOH solution at a time, until you begin to see pink flashing through the mixture. Then start adding NaOH in drops. Gently swirl the flask after each NaOH addition.

At the end point, read the meniscus level and estimate to the nearest 0.01 mL. Record this final NaOH buret reading in the column headed "determination 1".

13. Refill the buret with your NaOH solution. Titrate a second vinegar sample in a second 125-mL Erlenmeyer flask, repeating Steps 5–12. Record your data in the column headed "determination 2".

14. Drain the remaining NaOH solution from your buret into the Discarded Solutions beaker. Rinse the buret with tap water. Transfer the rinses to the Discarded Solutions beaker.

Rinse the buret twice with distilled water. Transfer the rinses into the Discarded Solutions beaker. With the stopcock open, invert the buret, and clamp it to the support stand for drying.

15. Repeat Step 14 with your vinegar buret.

16. Empty the titration mixtures from the Erlenmeyer flasks into the drain. Rinse the flasks with tap water and then with distilled water.

Pour the remaining vinegar into the Discarded Solutions beaker. Rinse the vinegar beaker with tap water and then with distilled water. Transfer the rinses into the Discarded Solutions beaker.

17. Unless your laboratory instructor indicates otherwise, pour any remaining standard NaOH solution into the Discarded Solutions beaker. Rinse the flask with tap water and then with distilled water. Discard the rinses into the Discarded Solutions beaker.

IV. Neutralizing Your Discarded Solutions

CAUTION

$6M$ HCl is a toxic, corrosive solution that can cause skin burns.

18. Add 2–3 drops of phenolphthalein solution to the Discarded Solutions beaker. Gently swirl the beaker to mix. If the resulting solution is not pink, consult with your laboratory instructor.

   Add $6M$ hydrochloric acid (HCl) dropwise to the Discarded Solutions beaker, mixing well with a glass stirring rod after each addition. Continue adding HCl solution dropwise just until the solution becomes colorless. Pour the colorless solution into the drain. Rinse the beaker with tap water, then distilled water, pouring the rinses into the drain.

CAUTION

Wash your hands thoroughly with soap or detergent before leaving the laboratory.

Name   Partner   Section   Date

Post-Laboratory Questions

Use the spaces provided for the answers and additional paper if necessary.

1. Would the following procedural errors cause your calculated molarity of HOAc in vinegar to be too high, too low, or unchanged? Briefly explain your answer.

    (a) You forgot to rinse your wet buret with vinegar before you delivered the vinegar into the Erlenmeyer flask.

    (b) You delivered the vinegar into a wet Erlenmeyer flask.

    (c) You used a buret with a broken tip.

2. A student performing this experiment forgot to add phenolphthalein solution to the vinegar solution before beginning the titration. After adding 27 mL of NaOH solution, he realized his error and added the indicator. The solution turned bright pink. Suggest a procedure the student could follow to salvage the titration.

3. In Part IV of the Procedure, you added 6M HCl to the Discarded Solutions beaker containing excess NaOH solution. HCl reacts with NaOH as shown in Equation 5.

$$HCl(aq) + NaOH(aq) \rightarrow NaCl(aq) + H_2O(\ell) \tag{Eq. 5}$$

Briefly explain why it would be hazardous to dispose of either your NaOH solution or 6M HCl in the drain, yet it is safe to pour the reaction mixture you prepared in Part IV into the drain.

4. Acetic acid solutions called "cleaning vinegar" are effective in dissolving calcium carbonate deposits on shower tiles. What sample size of $0.9181M$ cleaning vinegar would require 27.50 mL of $0.5185M$ NaOH for neutralization?

5. Muriatic acid is a concentrated HCl solution available in the hardware department of some stores. What mass of baking soda (sodium hydrogen carbonate, $NaHCO_3$) would be required to neutralize 10.00 mL of $12.1M$ muriatic acid remaining in a nearly empty bottle, so that the solution could be safely poured into the drain, and the bottle recycled? The reaction of $NaHCO_3$ with HCl is shown in Equation 6.

$$HCl(aq) + NaHCO_3(aq) \rightarrow NaCl(aq) + CO_2(g) + H_2O(\ell) \qquad \text{(Eq. 6)}$$

_____   _____   _____   _____
Name   *Partner*   *Section*   *Date*

Data and Observations

I. Preparing the Vinegar Sample for Titration

vinegar sample identification code   _____

	determination	
	1	2
initial vinegar buret reading, mL	_____	_____
final vinegar buret reading, mL	_____	_____
volume of vinegar sample transferred, mL	_____	_____

II. Preparing the NaOH Buret

concentration of NaOH solution, mol/L   _____

III. Titrating Vinegar

	determination	
	1	2
initial NaOH buret reading, mL	_____	_____
final NaOH buret reading, mL	_____	_____
volume of NaOH used for titration, mL	_____	_____

Calculations and Conclusions

Show your calculations in the spaces provided. Remember to include units with all calculated results.

1. Calculate the number of moles of NaOH required for the titration, using Equation 2.

determination 1 _____   determination 2 _____

2. Calculate the number of moles of HOAc titrated, using Equation 3.

determination 1 _____   determination 2 _____

3. Calculate the molarity of HOAc in the vinegar sample, using Equation 4.

determination 1 _____   determination 2 _____

4. Calculate the average molarity of HOAc in the vinegar sample, using Equation 7.

$$\text{average molarity, mol/L} = \frac{\text{molarity from determination 1} + \text{molarity from determination 2}}{2}$$

(Eq. 7)

average molarity _____

_____ _____ _____ _____
Name   *Partner*   *Section*   *Date*

Pre-Laboratory Assignment

1. With regard to the solutions you will use in this experiment, briefly explain why you are required to wear departmentally approved safety goggles while doing this experiment.

2. Briefly define the following terms:

(a) standard solution

(b) titration

(c) molarity

3. Why is it important that

    (a) there are no bubbles in the buret tip prior to beginning a titration of vinegar with NaOH solution?

    (b) you add phenolphthalein indicator solution to the vinegar solution prior to beginning the titration?

4. A student performing this experiment titrates 22.32 mL of vinegar with $0.5172M$ NaOH. The initial NaOH buret reading is 1.18 mL and the final NaOH buret reading is 21.35 mL. What is the molarity of HOAc in the vinegar sample?

Laboratory Techniques: Measuring the Volume of Liquids

Prepared by Norman E. Griswold, Nebraska Wesleyan University

PURPOSE OF THE EXPERIMENT

Use general chemistry laboratory volumetric ware. Clean and handle volumetric ware, and use it to measure liquid volumes. Use a volumetric flask to prepare solutions. Use a volumetric pipet and a buret for titrations.

BACKGROUND INFORMATION

Identifying Units for Volume Measurement

The basic unit of laboratory volume measurement is defined as a cube that measures exactly one meter on each side. The volume occupied by this cube is defined as one **cubic meter (m^3)**. However, because we seldom work with such large volumes in the laboratory, units smaller than a cubic meter are usually much more convenient to use.

For example, the volume of a cube that measures 10 centimeters (cm), or 1 decimeter (dm), on each side is the basis for one of the smaller volume units. Such a cube has a volume of 1000 cm^3 (or 1 dm^3), and this volume is defined as one **liter (L)**. One liter equals 0.001 m^3 or the volume of 1000 g of water under standard conditions. The volume of 0.001 L is defined as one **milliliter (mL)**, which means that 1 L contains 1000 mL. 1 mL is equal to one **cubic centimeter (cm^3)**, so the terms milliliter and cubic centimeter are used interchangeably. 1 mL also equals the volume of 1 g of water. Experiments performed in microscale require liquid volumes of less than 1 mL. For such experiments, the most common volume unit used is the **microliter (μL)**, which equals 0.001 mL.

Identifying Volumetric Ware

Several kinds of calibrated containers are available for measuring liquid volume. These containers, called **volumetric ware**, are labeled with one or more marks to indicate the volume they contain or deliver. For example, graduated cylinders are used for measuring approximate liquid volumes. Pipets and burets are used to more precisely measure liquid volumes of 1 mL or more. Pipetters and plastic graduated Beral pipets are used for precisely transferring liquids in volumes of less than 1 mL. Bottletop dispensers are used to dispense set amounts of reagents from stock bottles. Volumetric flasks are used for preparing solutions of known concentration.

A piece of volumetric ware is calibrated and labeled in terms of either the volume it can hold or the volume it can deliver. Manufacturers usually label their volumetric ware to indicate the type of calibration, using **TD** for "to deliver" and **TC** for "to contain". For example, a pipet marked TD 25-mL is calibrated to deliver 25.00 mL of liquid at a specified temperature, as long as it is filled to the calibration mark. A volumetric flask marked TC 100-mL is calibrated to contain 100.00 mL of liquid at a specified temperature, when the flask is filled to the calibration mark.

The volume of a given mass of liquid varies with temperature. Consequently, liquid volume measurements must be referenced to some standard temperature. The National Institute of Standards and Technology (NIST) uses 20.0 °C as the standard temperature for volume calibration. Most manufacturers label their volumetric ware with the temperature at which the calibration was performed, which is usually 20.0 °C. Let's examine the basic types of volumetric ware more closely.

Figure 1
Graduated cylinder

A. Graduated Cylinders

A **graduated cylinder**, shown in Figure 1, is used for measuring approximate liquid volumes. Graduated cylinders are made of either plastic or glass. They vary in capacity from 5 mL to 2000 mL. The subdivisions marked on the cylinders are usually in units of about 1% of the total volume: that is, 0.1 mL on a 10-mL cylinder, 1 mL on a 100-mL cylinder, and 5 mL on a 500-mL cylinder. Most cylinders are designated TD and equipped with a pouring spout. Many cylinders have a hexagonal base to prevent rolling if they fall over. An optional accessory for glass cylinders is a plastic guard that fits around the upper part of the cylinder. This guard absorbs the impact if the cylinder falls over.

B. Pipets

Pipets are designed to accurately deliver precisely measured liquid volumes. Two basic types of pipets are shown in Figure 2. A small rubber bulb, called a **pipet bulb**, must be placed over the top of a pipet to draw liquid into the pipet. The bulb is then removed to dispense the liquid.

The first basic type of pipet, called a **measuring pipet**, is used for delivering variable, but precisely measured, liquid volumes. Normally, the calibration marks on measuring pipets do not extend all the way to the tip. These pipets are drained from one calibration mark to another. The calibrations utilize units that make it convenient to accurately deliver intermediate volumes, up to the maximum capacity of the pipet. Measuring pipets with capacities from 0.1 mL to 10 mL are available. All are calibrated TD.

A **serological pipet** is a special kind of measuring pipet that has calibration marks extending to its tip. Serological pipets are available with capacities ranging from 0.1 mL to 10 mL. A ground-glass band near the top of the pipet indicates that, after free drainage has ceased, the small amount of liquid remaining in the tip must be blown out, using a pipet bulb, to obtain the total rated capacity. Serological pipets are used for delivering exact volumes of liquid samples to tubes or slides for medical tests.

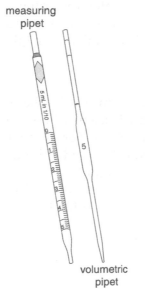

Figure 2
Measuring and volumetric pipets

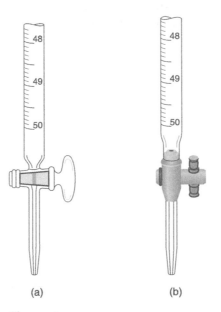

The other basic type of pipet is the **volumetric** or **transfer pipet**, which is used for delivering a single, fixed liquid volume. Volumetric pipets are calibrated with only one mark, indicating the full capacity, and are available with capacities ranging from 1 mL to 200 mL.

Manufacturers color-code both measuring and volumetric pipets with a color band near the top, to ease identification of the pipet capacity. For example, one manufacturer uses a blue band on 1-mL pipets, an orange band on 2-mL pipets, a white band on 10-mL pipets, and a red band on 50-mL pipets.

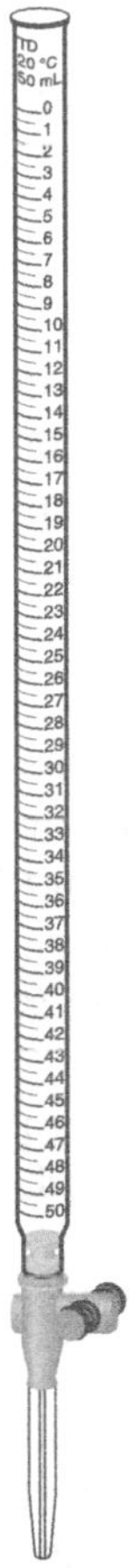

C. Burets

A **buret** is a long, narrow, calibrated tube with a valve, called a **stopcock**, at one end, which is used to control the flow of liquid (see Figure 3). Burets are available in 10-mL, 25-mL, 50-mL, and 100-mL sizes. They are labeled TD. The precision of measurement attainable using a buret is somewhat higher than that attainable using a measuring pipet.

Burets differ chiefly in the type of stopcock used. Two common types of stopcocks are: a tapered glass stopcock in a glass barrel, shown in Figure 4(a); and a Teflon stopcock in a glass or Teflon barrel, shown in Figure 4(b).

D. Volumetric Flasks

Volumetric flasks have a large glass bulb attached to a long narrow neck, labeled with a single calibration mark. They are sealed using a plastic cap or tightly fitting stopper (see Figure 5). The calibration mark is located on the narrow neck to allow filling to a reproducible volume. Volumetric flasks vary in capacity from 5 mL to 5 L. These flasks are calibrated TC and are commonly used for preparing solutions.

Figure 3
A buret

(a)   (b)

Figure 4
Two common buret stopcock types

Figure 5
Volumetric flask

E. Some Special Volumetric Ware

In this section, some special kinds of burets and pipets are described briefly. Use of these unusual types is currently increasing in chemistry laboratories, especially for small-scale experiments.

1. **Beral pipets** are small, disposable, one-piece plastic pipets, approximately 15 cm long (see Figure 6). They are made in several styles, one of which is the graduated Beral pipet shown in the figure. Graduated Beral pipets have an approximate capacity of 5 mL, with graduations for each milliliter. They are particularly useful for dispensing small liquid volumes. Beral pipets are also used for small-scale titrations, because they deliver reproducible drop sizes.

2. **Pipetters** are plastic devices that permit the user to accurately dispense liquid samples with one hand, leaving the other hand free for stirring or other activities. Pipetters use plunger-operated pistons to take up and dispense liquids. Special tips are attached at the bottom of the pipetters. For ease in selection, pipetter tips are color-coded to match the plunger on the pipetter body. Figure 7 shows a typical pipetter.

   Pipetters are available in various fixed-volume sizes, ranging from 1 to 2500 μL, and in several adjustable-volume ranges, such as 2–20 μL and 100–1000 μL. Use of a pipetter permits rapid, repeated, accurate small-volume liquid transfers. The tips are disposable, and the pipetter body can be sterilized by autoclaving.

3. **Bottletop dispensers** are plastic devices that fit on top of reagent bottles. They consist of a graduated measuring tube, with a plunger at the top, and a dispensing tube for delivering preset liquid volumes extending from the side of the measuring tube. Dispensers have adjustable volume ranges, such as 0.5–6.0 mL or 5–25 mL. The desired volume is set and locked on the measuring tube. Then the plunger is raised and depressed to deliver the preset liquid volume. Bottletop dispensers should not be used to dispense concentrated acids, hydrocarbons, oils, organic solvents, or oxidizing acids, because such substances may react with the materials of the dispenser.

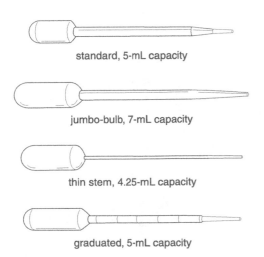

standard, 5-mL capacity

jumbo-bulb, 7-mL capacity

thin stem, 4.25-mL capacity

graduated, 5-mL capacity

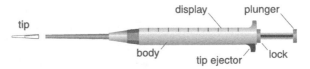

Figure 6
Beral pipets

Figure 7
An adjustable-volume pipetter

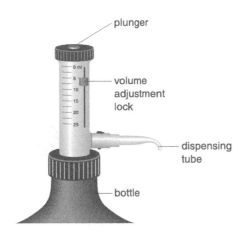

Figure 8
A bottle-top dispenser

Cleaning Volumetric Ware

Volumetric ware must be thoroughly clean before each use. Any grease or other contaminants present will affect the accuracy of any measurement made using volumetric ware. Foreign material may react with a solution, altering its concentration. In some cases, foreign material may dissolve in the solution and then contaminate the experiment in which the solution is used.

For all these reasons, chemists normally empty, clean, thoroughly rinse, and drain each piece of volumetric ware immediately after use. After the final rinsing and draining, a uniform, often nearly invisible, film of water should adhere to the inner surface of the container. The appearance of uneven wetting or droplets on the inner surface is a sign that the item requires further cleaning.

Burets with glass stopcocks are especially likely to become contaminated, due to the spreading of stopcock grease over the inside wall. A **buret brush**, which looks like a test tube brush with a very long handle, is used to clean a buret. Note that the brush bristles should not be pushed past the bottom calibration mark. When a buret is rinsed, the rinse water should be discharged through the buret tip. This technique reduces the possibility of stopcock grease spreading to the interior of the buret.

Volumetric ware that must be dry before reuse is usually left standing in air at room temperature, rather than being heated. These containers will expand on heating and, after cooling, may be distorted from their original form. Distorted volumetric ware may not contain or deliver the calibrated volume. Therefore, drying volumetric ware with a flame, hot plate, or oven is not normally recommended.

Reading the Liquid Level in Volumetric Ware

The scale marked on a piece of volumetric ware must be noted carefully, before attempting to read the volume of liquid it contains. For example, the upper end of the scale on a graduated cylinder is at the top of the cylinder, while the upper end of the scale on a buret is at the stopcock end.

The position of the liquid level in volumetric ware must also be carefully noted. In a plastic cylinder, the liquid surface is flat, so the level is relatively easy to read. However, in a glass cylinder, the liquid surface forms a curve, or **meniscus**. For most liquids, the curve is concave (downward), and the position of the ***bottom*** of the meniscus must be read to accurately determine the liquid volume. However, for a few liquids, such as

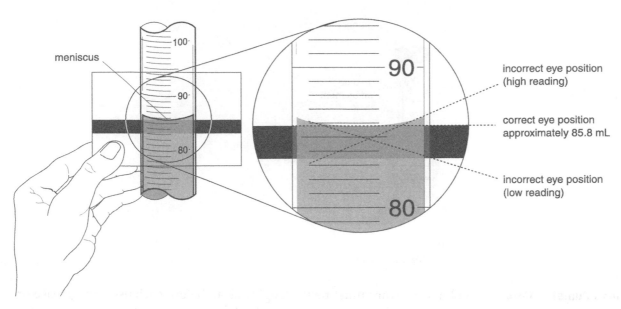

Figure 9
Reading a meniscus

mercury, the curve is convex (upward). In such cases, the position of the **top** of the meniscus must be read to accurately determine the liquid volume.

When reading liquid volumes, your eye must be level with the bottom of the meniscus (assuming that the meniscus is concave), in order for you to observe the correct volume (see Figure 9). For example, when reading the liquid level in a graduated cylinder, if your eye is above the bottom of the meniscus, you will observe too high a reading. If your eye is below the bottom of the meniscus, you will observe too low a reading. This apparent variation in volume caused by viewing from different angles is due to an optical phenomenon called **parallax**. Proper reading of the meniscus level, which includes avoiding error due to parallax, is an important part of the use of all volumetric ware.

In this experiment, you will clean all of your glassware before use. As you use a graduated cylinder to measure liquid volumes, you will carefully note the position of the meniscus and read it with your eye at that level, in order to get an accurate reading. You will prepare dilute solutions of sodium hydroxide (NaOH) and of hydrochloric acid (HCl) for use in several titrations. You will repeat each titration four times, in order to check your titration **precision**; that is, how close successive determinations are to each other. At the end of the experiment, you will discard any acid or base solution remaining, as your laboratory instructor directs. Finally, you will clean, rinse, and drain all your glassware.

PROCEDURE

CHEMICAL ALERT

6*M* **hydrochloric acid—corrosive and toxic**
6*M* **sodium hydroxide—corrosive and toxic**
1% phenolphthalein—flammable

CAUTION

Wear departmentally approved safety goggles while doing this experiment.

I. Cleaning Volumetric Ware

A. Cleaning Graduated Cylinders

Rinse each cylinder with tap water. Add a dilute detergent or soap solution, and use an appropriate brush to scrub each cylinder. Pour the detergent solution into the drain, and rinse each cylinder twice with tap water. Finally, rinse each cylinder three times with small amounts of distilled or deionized water. Invert the cylinders, and allow them to drain.

B. Cleaning a Pipet

NOTE: Do not use a pipet bulb that has been contaminated by a liquid. If you are right-handed, hold the bulb in your left hand, as shown in Figure 11(a) later in this experiment. Make certain that the connection between the bulb and pipet is secure enough to prevent air leaks. Some pipet bulbs fit over the end of the pipet, while others are designed to be held tightly against the top of the pipet.

CAUTION

Never **attempt to draw liquid into a pipet using your mouth. You could easily inhale some of the liquid.** ***Always*** **use a pipet bulb.**

Half fill a 250-mL beaker with detergent solution. Place the bulb on the pipet. Squeeze the bulb, and then lower the pipet tip into the detergent solution. Slowly release the bulb to draw detergent solution into the pipet, until the pipet is about one-third full. Remove the bulb from the pipet, and quickly place your right forefinger (or your left forefinger, if you are left-handed) over the top of the pipet.

Holding the pipet nearly horizontally, carefully roll it about the long axis so that the solution contacts the entire interior surface. Thoroughly cleaning the area above the calibration marks is usually not necessary, but the rest of the pipet *must* be clean. Return the pipet to an upright position, and remove your finger to allow the solution through the pipet tip, back into the beaker.

NOTE: Do not rinse a pipet by holding it under running water.

Using the bulb, draw a small amount of tap water into the pipet. Hold the pipet horizontally as described above, rotate it, and then drain the rinse water through the tip into the sink. Repeat the tap water rinse two more times. Then rinse the pipet three times with distilled water.

The appearance of uneven wetting or droplets on the pipet walls indicates that further cleaning is necessary. Check with your laboratory instructor for direction.

C. Cleaning a Buret

Attach your buret to a buret clamp mounted on a ring stand. Pour distilled water into the buret. Open the stopcock and allow the water to drain through the tip into a beaker. Only a uniform, nearly invisible, film of water should remain on the interior surface. If any droplets appear on the interior wall, the buret is dirty.

Use a buret brush and detergent solution to clean a dirty buret. Open the stopcock. Dip the brush into warm detergent solution. Carefully insert the brush into the top of the buret. Scrub the inner buret wall, being careful not to push the brush past the bottom calibration mark. Remove the brush, and add small amounts of tap water to the buret. Allow the water to drain through the buret tip each time. Repeat the rinsing and draining until the buret appears free of detergent solution.

Add a few milliliters of distilled water to the buret, making sure that the water contacts the entire inner surface. Completely drain the water through the tip. Repeat the rinsing and draining process twice more, using a few more milliliters of distilled water each time. Three small portions of distilled water added and drained in this manner will completely remove all the tap water and replace it with a film of distilled water. After the final rinsing and draining, a uniform, nearly invisible, film of distilled water should remain on the inner buret wall. Uneven wetting or droplets on the inner wall are signs that the buret requires further cleaning. If this occurs, check with your laboratory instructor for direction.

Before using a clean buret, confirm that the stopcock does not leak. To do so, attach the buret to a ring stand. Fill it with water. Observe the stopcock for a short time, looking for any signs of leaking. Consult your laboratory instructor if your buret leaks.

Teflon stopcocks do not need lubrication. Glass stopcocks, on the other hand, require constant lubrication with a thin film of stopcock grease. To lubricate a glass stopcock, carefully remove the tapered glass plug from the barrel. Wipe all the old grease from the surfaces of both the plug and the barrel, paying particular attention to the hole in the plug through which liquid flows. Spread a thin layer of stopcock grease over the plug surface, being careful to avoid the area near the hole. Insert the plug into the barrel. Rotate the plug several complete revolutions in one direction. If the proper amount of grease has been used, the stopcock will appear nearly transparent where the plug contacts the barrel and the plug will turn freely. On some burets, a metal clip can be attached to the inserted glass plug to help prevent it from falling out.

II. Measuring Liquids in a Graduated Cylinder

NOTE: To measure a liquid in a graduated cylinder, pour the liquid into the cylinder up to the desired volume. Locate the meniscus level, adjust the position of your eye to avoid a parallax error, and read the liquid volume. If you have added too much liquid, pour the excess into a discard container, **not** back into the reagent supply bottle. Remember that volumes measured using graduated cylinders are only approximate. Therefore, extra care must be taken to make accurate readings, in order to introduce as little additional error as possible.

In Part III, you will prepare solutions by measuring 2.5 mL of liquid with a graduated cylinder. The following exercise will help you better appreciate the approximate nature of graduated cylinder readings.

Pour about 2.5 mL of distilled water into your clean 10-mL graduated cylinder. To avoid parallax error, make sure your line of vision is level with the bottom of the meniscus each time you read the water volume. Read the position of the bottom of the meniscus. Add water, if necessary. When you have measured 2.5 mL of water as exactly as you can, pour the water from the 10-mL cylinder into your 100-mL cylinder. Add 2.5 mL more water to the 10-mL cylinder. Add this second 2.5 mL of water to the water already in your 100-mL cylinder. Measure two more 2.5-mL portions of water in your 10-mL cylinder. Add each 2.5-mL portion to the water in your 100-mL cylinder.

Now read the total volume of water in your 100-mL cylinder. Record the total volume on your Data Sheet. Calculate the average volume of each 2.5-mL addition, and record the result. Pour the water in the 100-mL cylinder into the drain.

Repeat the above water-measuring process using the 10-mL and 100-mL cylinders two more times. Then, if you are satisfied that you can accurately measure the volume of water in a graduated cylinder, save your last 10 mL of water in the 100-mL cylinder. Ask your laboratory instructor to check your measurements and calculations. Your laboratory instructor will initial your Data Sheet or laboratory notebook to indicate that you have mastered the technique.

Pour the water in the 100-mL cylinder into the drain. Invert both cylinders, and allow to dry.

III. Preparing Solutions Using a Volumetric Flask

NOTE: Solutions of known concentrations can be prepared in volumetric flasks. If the solute is a solid or a concentrated acid, follow the guidelines provided by your laboratory instructor. If the solute is a liquid or you are diluting a more concentrated solution, use the procedure described in this section. After using a volumetric flask to prepare a solution, thoroughly rinse the flask with distilled water, and invert it to dry. Store the dry flask with the stopper in place. If the stopper is made of glass, insert a small strip of paper between the stopper and the flask mouth, so the stopper will not stick.

NOTE: Usually, solutions should not be stored in volumetric flasks for any length of time. This is especially true for alkaline solutions, because bases can react with glass. Therefore, you should transfer prepared solutions into clean, dry, labeled containers.

A. Mixing a Dilute NaOH Solution

CAUTION

NaOH solutions are toxic and corrosive, and they can cause burns. If you spill any solution, immediately notify your laboratory instructor.

Measure 2.5 mL of 6M NaOH in your 10-mL graduated cylinder. Remove the stopper from a 250-mL volumetric flask. Using a funnel, slowly pour the 2.5 mL of NaOH solution into the flask. Again using the funnel, add 200 mL of distilled water to the flask, while slowly swirling the flask to agitate the solution. Slowly add more distilled water until the liquid level is just a bit below the calibration mark on the flask neck. Use a small dropper or a Beral pipet to add the final amount of water needed to raise the bottom

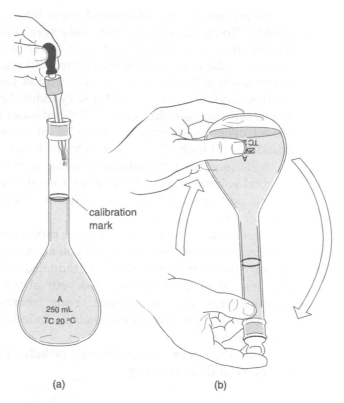

calibration mark

A
250 mL
TC 20 °C

(a)   (b)

Figure 10
Preparing solutions using a volumetric flask

of the meniscus to the calibration mark (see Figure 10(a)). Be sure to avoid parallax error when reading the final liquid level. When the bottom of the meniscus aligns with the calibration mark, stopper the flask. Holding the stopper firmly in place with your index finger, slowly invert the flask, end over end, 20–30 times to make a homogeneous solution (see Figure 10(b)).

Carefully pour the solution from the flask into a 400-mL beaker labeled "dil. NaOH". When all of the solution has drained from the flask, thoroughly rinse the flask with tap water, then, distilled water. Rinse the 10-mL graduated cylinder with tap water, then distilled water. Invert both to dry.

B. Mixing a Dilute HCl Solution

CAUTION

Hydrochloric acid solutions are toxic and corrosive, and they can cause burns. If you spill any solution, immediately notify your laboratory instructor.

Dilute 2.5 mL of 6*M* HCl, using the technique in Part III*A*. Label a 400-mL beaker "dil. HCl", and use it to store your diluted solution.

After you have mixed and transferred your solution, thoroughly rinse the flask and graduated cylinder with tap water, then, distilled water. Invert the glassware to dry.

IV. Transferring Liquids Using a Volumetric Pipet

Pour a small amount of the solution you wish to transfer into a clean, dry 250-mL beaker. Your laboratory instructor will tell you which solution to use. Attach a pipet bulb to a volumetric pipet. Squeeze the bulb, and insert the pipet tip into the solution. Then slowly release pressure on the bulb to draw solution into the pipet, until the pipet is about one-third full. During this procedure, keep the tip well below the liquid surface, as shown in Figure 11(b), so that you do not draw any air into the pipet along with the solution. By releasing pressure on the bulb slowly, you can control the filling rate and avoid drawing solution into the bulb, which would contaminate the bulb.

Quickly remove the bulb, and place your right forefinger (or your left, if you are left-handed) on top of the pipet, in order to prevent the solution from draining out, as shown in Figure 11(c). Hold the pipet so it is nearly horizontal. Roll the pipet around the long axis so the solution contacts the entire interior surface. Remove your finger briefly during this process, in order to allow the solution to enter the upper pipet stem.

Holding the pipet upright again, lift your finger and allow the solution to drain out through the tip into an appropriately labeled discard container. Discard this solution as directed by your laboratory instructor. Repeat this procedure with at least two more portions of the solution.

Next, use the pipet to transfer a measured volume of the same solution from the beaker into a 250-mL Erlenmeyer flask. Fully squeeze the bulb, and insert the pipet tip into the solution. Draw solution into the pipet, up to a level above the calibration mark on the pipet, being careful not to draw solution into the bulb.

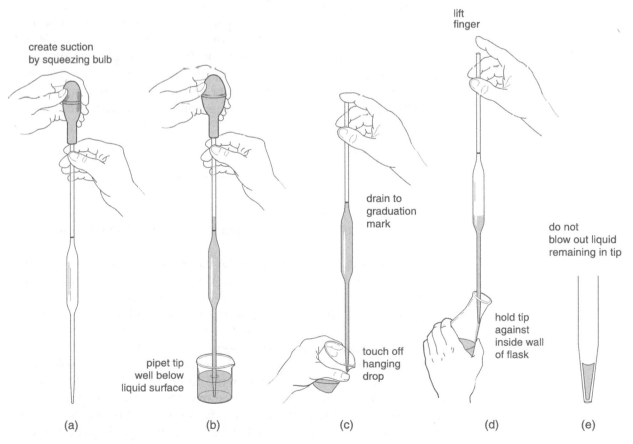

Figure 11

Using a volumetric pipet

Lightly rest the pipet tip against the bottom of the beaker, and gently remove the bulb. Quickly press your forefinger on top of the pipet, as before. Do not allow the liquid level to fall below the calibration mark. Remove the pipet from the solution. Wipe the outside of the lower stem and tip with clean, absorbent tissue.

Holding the pipet vertically, slowly drain some of the solution back into the beaker, until the bottom of the meniscus exactly aligns with the calibration mark. Rotating the pipet top against your forefinger may help you control the liquid release rate more easily. When the bottom of the meniscus is at the calibration mark, touch the pipet tip against the inner wall of the beaker, so that the hanging drop on the tip is transferred to the beaker, as shown in Figure 11(c).

Slowly move the pipet to the 250-mL Erlenmeyer flask into which you wish to transfer the measured solution. Hold the pipet tip against the inner wall of the flask, in order to avoid splatter. Lift your forefinger to allow the solution to drain from the pipet, as shown in Figure 11(d).

When the liquid flow stops, hold the pipet vertically for 15 s more to allow for complete draining. Then touch the pipet tip to the inner wall of the flask, so that the hanging drop is transferred to the flask. However, do *not* attempt to blow out the small amount of solution remaining in the pipet tip. These pipets are calibrated to deliver a specified volume of liquid *excluding* the liquid remaining in the tip, as shown in Figure 11(e).

Dispose of the solution as directed by your laboratory instructor. Clean and invert all glassware to dry.

Perform the following exercise to gain dexterity with a volumetric pipet. Using a clean volumetric pipet and the previously described technique, transfer exactly 25.00 mL of distilled water from a 250-mL beaker into the 250-mL Erlenmeyer flask. Repeat the process until you successfully complete at least three transfers in a row. Then ask your laboratory instructor to initial your Data Sheet or laboratory notebook to indicate that you have successfully learned proper pipetting technique.

V. Using a Buret

NOTE: You do not need to record data for Parts V*A* and V*B*.

A. Filling and Draining a Buret

Clamp a clean 50-mL buret to a ring stand. Prepare the buret as described in Part I*C*.

When the buret is clean and ready for use, rinse it three times with small portions of the solution to be dispensed. Your laboratory instructor will tell you what solution to use. After each addition, allow the solution to drain through the buret tip into an appropriately labeled discard container. Discard this rinse solution as directed by your laboratory instructor.

Close the stopcock. Place a short-stem funnel in the buret. Slowly pour solution through the funnel into the buret. Do not allow the solution to overflow the funnel. Fill the buret until the liquid level is above the 0.00-mL calibration mark at the top. Then, remove the funnel, to prevent any solution dripping from it into the buret during the rest of the procedure.

Eliminate any air bubbles in the buret tip by opening the stopcock completely for a second or two, in order to quickly release a little solution and any bubbles into the discard container. Then drain more solution until the bottom of the meniscus aligns with, or is slightly below, the 0.00-mL mark. It is not necessary to exactly align the liquid level with the 0.00-mL mark, as long as you read and record the liquid level at this point, before you proceed further. Finally, touch the buret tip to a wet glass surface to remove the hanging drop.

NOTE: Buret calibrations increase in value from top to bottom, the reverse of most volumetric ware calibration scales.

A 50-mL buret is calibrated in 0.1-mL units, but one-fifth of a unit can be reproducibly estimated. Therefore, you should always estimate the liquid level if it is between calibration marks, and record every reading to the nearest 0.02 mL.

Read the liquid level in the buret with great care. To facilitate more accurate reading, use a white card with a dark stripe on it. Hold the card directly behind the buret, with the top of the black stripe slightly below the meniscus, as shown in Figure 12.

Burets with glass stopcocks. Burets with glass stopcocks must be manipulated carefully, to avoid loosening the stopcock plug and causing a leak. Using your right hand to operate a stopcock handle oriented on the right side of the buret usually loosens the stopcock. Figure 13 on the next page shows the preferred method. In the figure, note that, although the stopcock handle is on the right, it is being manipulated with the left hand. While turning the handle, you should apply light pressure toward the buret with your left hand, to prevent the plug from slipping out of the barrel. However, be careful not to touch your left palm to the stopcock or the plug could loosen. This procedure leaves the right hand free to swirl the solution in the receiving flask.

Burets with Teflon stopcocks. When using burets with Teflon stopcocks, you can operate the stopcock with either hand, without any risk of the plug slipping out.

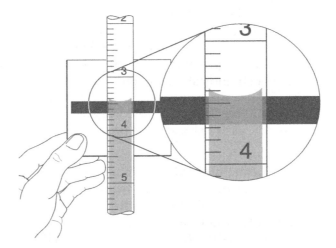

Figure 12
Reading the liquid level in a buret

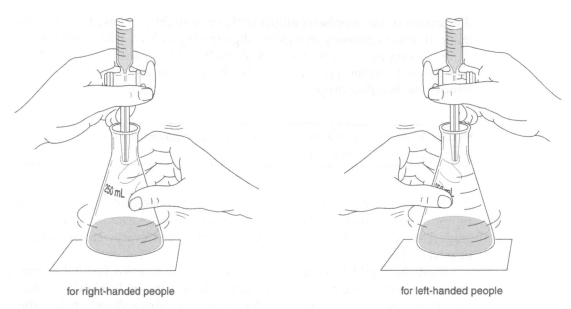

for right-handed people   for left-handed people

Figure 13
Manipulating a glass stopcock

You should drain solution from a buret slowly so that the film of solution on the buret wall will drain reproducibly. After you have drained the desired volume, touch a glass stirring rod to the buret tip, to remove the hanging drop. Use a wash bottle to rinse the stirring rod with distilled water, allowing the rinses to run into the receiving flask. After a brief pause, record the final buret reading.

When you are finished using the buret, drain the excess solution and dispose of it as instructed. Rinse the buret thoroughly with tap water, then with distilled water. Clamp it to a ring stand with the stopcock open, and let it drain dry.

B. Recognizing Titration End Points

Rinse your buret with your dilute NaOH solution. Discard the rinses as directed by your laboratory instructor.

Fill the buret with your dilute NaOH solution.

Using a graduated cylinder, transfer approximately 5–10 mL of your dilute HCl solution into a clean 250-mL Erlenmeyer flask.

Add approximately 30 mL of distilled water and 2–3 drops of phenolphthalein indicator solution to the HCl solution in the flask.

NOTE: Phenolphthalein is colorless in acidic solution and pink in basic solution. The solution will turn pink when the reaction reaches its end point.

Titrate the acid solution to the end point. You will know that the end point has been reached, when the addition of one drop of NaOH solution changes the colorless solution to a very faint pink that persists for at least 20 s after vigorous swirling.

Add 5–10 mL more of your dilute HCl solution to the flask. Titrate the added HCl solution to the end point.

Repeat the previous step until you can attain consistent end points.

In order to ensure that you are reading the buret correctly, ask your laboratory instructor to check your buret reading at the end of one of your titrations. If your technique is correct, your laboratory instructor will initial your Data Sheet or laboratory notebook.

Empty the solution in the Erlenmeyer flask into the sink. Rinse the flask with tap water, then, distilled water. Rinse your buret with distilled water. Allow both to drain to dry.

C. Checking Your Titration Precision

NOTE: Record your data for this part of the experiment on your Data Sheet or in your laboratory notebook. Record all buret readings to the nearest 0.02 mL.

Refill the buret with dilute NaOH solution. Record your initial buret reading.

Rinse your volumetric pipet with your dilute HCl solution. Discard the rinses as directed by your laboratory instructor.

Pipet exactly 25.00 mL of dilute HCl solution into a clean 250-mL Erlenmeyer flask.

Add 2–3 drops of phenolphthalein indicator solution to the flask.

Titrate the HCl solution to the end point. Record your final buret reading.

Pour the solution in the Erlenmeyer flask into the sink. Rinse the flask once with tap water, then, distilled water.

Transfer another 25.00 mL of dilute HCl solution into the flask. Repeat the above titration procedure, recording all data on your Data Sheet or in your laboratory notebook.

Repeat the titration procedure until you obtain three required NaOH solution volumes that are within 0.1 mL of each other.

VI. Neutralizing Discarded Solutions for Disposal

Drain any remaining NaOH solution from the buret into the beaker containing your dilute NaOH solution. Pour any remaining dilute HCl solution into the dilute NaOH solution to make a neutral solution. Use pH paper to check that the solution is neutral. Pour the neutral mixture into the drain, diluting with a large amount of running water. Rinse your glassware with tap water, then, distilled water. Thoroughly rinse the buret with tap water, then, distilled water.

CAUTION

Wash your hands thoroughly with soap or detergent before leaving the laboratory.

CALCULATIONS

Do the following calculations and record the results on your Data Sheet or in your laboratory notebook.

V. Using a Buret

C. Checking Your Titration Precision

1. Calculate the volume of dilute NaOH solution required for each titration.

2. Calculate the average volume of NaOH solution required for all of your titrations. Do not include data from any titration in which you failed to stop the titration at the end point.

3. For each determination, calculate the difference between the volume of dilute NaOH solution required and the average volume of NaOH solution determined in Calculation 2.

_____   _____   _____
Name   *Section*   *Date*

Post-Laboratory Questions

(Use the spaces provided for the answers and additional paper if necessary.)

1. Briefly explain why it was important to rinse the 10-mL graduated cylinder after you measured the 6*M* NaOH, before you measured the 6*M* HCl.

2. A student titrated two dilute HCl samples of equal volume. At the start of the first titration, she neglected to remove an air bubble from the buret tip. The air bubble was no longer present by the beginning of the second titration. The precision of her titration results was not good. Briefly explain whether the apparent titrant volume for the first titration was larger or smaller than that for the second titration, and why.

3. A student titrated two dilute HCl samples of equal volume, each measured using a volumetric pipet. The titration end points were reached correctly, but the volume required for the first titration was smaller than the volume required for the second. Briefly explain what might have caused the poor precision in the results.

4. Briefly explain why a volumetric pipet with a chipped or broken tip is usually useless, while a buret with a chipped or broken tip can still deliver accurate volumes.

5. Explain any differences you calculated between the volume of dilute NaOH solution required for each titration and the average volume of NaOH solution required.

Name _Section_ _Date_

Data Sheet

II. Measuring Liquids in a Graduated Cylinder

total volume of water in 100-mL cylinder, mL _____ _____ _____

average volume of each addition, mL _____ _____ _____

laboratory instructor initials _____

IV. Transferring Liquids Using a Volumetric Pipet

laboratory instructor initials _____

V. Using a Buret

B. _Recognizing Titration End Points_

laboratory instructor initials _____

C. _Checking Your Titration Precision_

	determination			
	_1_	_2_	_3_	_4_
volume of dilute HCl titrated, mL	_____	_____	_____	_____
final buret reading, mL	_____	_____	_____	_____
initial buret reading, mL	_____	_____	_____	_____
volume of dilute NaOH required, mL	_____	_____	_____	_____
average volume of dilute NaOH required, mL*		_____		
difference between the volume of dilute NaOH required for each titration and the average volume of dilute NaOH required, mL	_____	_____	_____	_____

* Exclude titrations in which you went beyond the end point.

Name   Section   Date

Pre-Laboratory Assignment

1. Why should you take extra care when handling the 6*M* NaOH and 6*M* HCl solutions for this experiment?

2. What does the designation "TD" mean? What kind of volumetric ware has this designation printed on it?

3. What is the difference between a pipet and a pipetter?

4. What is the name of the device used to control liquid flow from a buret?

5. **(a)** What is a meniscus?

(b) What part of the meniscus should be used to read the volume of liquid in a glass graduated cylinder?

6. **(a)** Briefly define the term parallax, as it relates to this experiment.

(b) Briefly explain how you can avoid a parallax error when using volumetric glassware.

7. Describe the correct method for transferring liquid with a pipet.

8. After filling a buret and removing the funnel, what should you do next?

Separating the Components of a Ternary Mixture

Prepared by H. Anthony Neidig, J. Iskowitz, and M. Royer,
Lebanon Valley College

PURPOSE OF THE EXPERIMENT

Separate the components of a mixture of sand, sodium chloride, and calcium carbonate. Calculate the percentage of each component in the mixture and the percent recovery of the components.

BACKGROUND INFORMATION

Some naturally occurring materials are mixtures of two or more substances. **Homogeneous mixtures** appear to be uniform throughout. You cannot see the individual particles of the components. Common examples of homogeneous mixtures are air, cola drink, and rubbing alcohol. **Heterogeneous mixtures** are not uniform throughout. You can often see the individual particles of the components. Rocks and soil are examples of such mixtures.

A variety of methods are available for separating the components of a mixture. **Physical methods** of separation use differences in the physical properties of the components of a mixture, such as solubility or boiling point. **Chemical methods** of separation involve the selective reaction of one of the components of a mixture to form a new substance. After the completion of the reaction, one of the physical properties of the new substance is used to separate it from the mixture. Generally, a second reaction is then used to reconvert the new substance to its original form.

In this experiment, you will separate the components of a **ternary mixture,** that is a mixture containing three substances. You will use five methods of separation, four physical and one chemical. In the following paragraphs, we will demonstrate the use of each of these methods in separating the components of a **binary mixture,** that is, a mixture containing two components.

Separating the Components of a Mixture by Physical Methods

Decantation is a process for separating the liquid component of a solid–liquid mixture from the solid by pouring. The solid is allowed to settle to the bottom of the container. The liquid is carefully poured from the vessel containing the mixture without disturbing the solid. This liquid is called the **supernatant liquid,** or the **supernate.** For example, we can separate the components of a heterogeneous mixture of solid silver chloride (AgCl) and water by decantation. To do this, we would carefully pour the supernatant liquid, water, from the vessel containing the insoluble AgCl.

Filtration is a process for separating a solid from a liquid by passing the liquid through a porous material such as filter paper. The solid is unable to pass through the pores in the filter paper and remains on the filter paper. This solid is called the **residue.** The liquid that passes through the paper is called the **filtrate.** For example, we can separate the components of a heterogeneous mixture of solid AgCl and water by filtration. In such a separation, AgCl is the residue, and water is the filtrate.

Evaporation is a separation process in which a solution is heated to remove the solvent. The substance, or residue, remaining after the solvent has evaporated is the substance originally dissolved in the solvent. For example, we can separate the components of a homogeneous mixture of potassium bromide (KBr) dissolved in water by evaporation. When we heat the solution, the solvent, water, evaporates, leaving the residue, KBr.

Extraction is a separation process that can be used when one component of a binary mixture is soluble in an added solvent and the other is not. The component that is insoluble in the extracting solvent can be recovered by removing the solvent containing the dissolved component by filtration. For example, we can separate the components of a heterogeneous mixture of solid KBr and solid AgCl by extraction with water. When we place the mixture in water, KBr dissolves and AgCl does not. We can then recover the AgCl by filtration. Finally, we can evaporate the water from the filtrate to recover the KBr.

Separating the Components of a Mixture by Chemical Methods

The chemical methods used to separate the components of a mixture involve the selective reaction of a substance with one or more of the components of the mixture. For example, we can separate the components of a heterogeneous mixture of solid barium sulfate ($BaSO_4$) and solid nickel(II) carbonate ($NiCO_3$) by the following chemical method.

If we add $3M$ hydrochloric acid (HCl) to the mixture, the aqueous HCl reacts with the solid $NiCO_3$, as shown in Equation 1. Barium sulfate does not react with $3M$ HCl, nor does it dissolve in the aqueous solution. Hence, $BaSO_4$ is not shown in Equation 1.

$$NiCO_3(s) + 2\,HCl(aq) \rightarrow NiCl_2(aq) + CO_2(g) + H_2O(l) \qquad \text{(Eq. 1)}$$

After separating the insoluble $BaSO_4$ from the reaction mixture by filtration, we add potassium carbonate (K_2CO_3) solution to the filtrate. Aqueous K_2CO_3 reacts with aqueous $NiCl_2$, forming insoluble $NiCO_3$, as shown in Equation 2. We recover the $NiCO_3$ by a second filtration.

$$NiCl_2(aq) + K_2CO_3(aq) \rightleftharpoons NiCO_3(s) + 2\,KCl(aq) \qquad \text{(Eq. 2)}$$

In this experiment, you will use the different physical and chemical properties of the components of a mixture of sand (SiO_2), sodium chloride (NaCl), and calcium carbonate ($CaCO_3$) to separate each of these substances from the mixture. Some of the physical and chemical properties of these three substances are listed in Table 1.

Table 1 *Selected physical and chemical properties of several compounds*

	Soluble in H_2O	*Reacts with 3M HCl*
SiO_2	no	no
NaCl	yes	no
$CaCO_3$	no	yes
$CaSO_4$	no	no
$Ca(NO_3)_2$	yes	no

The flowchart in Figure 1 summarizes the different steps you will take in this experiment. A **flowchart** is a schematic representation of a series of operations. Constructing a flowchart as you do an experiment is an effective way of recording your data and observations.

As shown in the flowchart, you will extract the NaCl from the mixture with water. You will use gravity filtration to separate the insoluble SiO_2 and $CaCO_3$ from the aqueous solution of NaCl. **Gravity filtration** is a process in which gravity draws a solution through filter paper held in a filtering funnel. You will recover NaCl from the filtrate by evaporating the water. When you add aqueous HCl to the residue from the filtration, $CaCO_3$ will react, as shown in Equation 3. Because SiO_2 does not react with aqueous HCl, the SiO_2 is not shown in Equation 3.

$$CaCO_3(s) + 2\ HCl(aq) \rightarrow CaCl_2(aq) + CO_2(g) + H_2O(l) \qquad \text{(Eq. 3)}$$

You will decant the supernatant liquid from the unreacted SiO_2. You will then add $1M\ K_2CO_3$ solution to the supernatant liquid to precipitate $CaCO_3$, as shown in Equation 4. Vacuum filtration or gravity filtration can be used to recover the insoluble $CaCO_3$. **Vacuum filtration** is a process in which an applied vacuum draws a solution through filter paper held in a Büchner funnel. The filtrate, containing the soluble KCl, is discarded, because it is of no interest to us in this experiment.

$$CaCl_2(aq) + K_2CO_3(aq) \rightleftharpoons CaCO_3(s) + 2\ KCl(aq) \qquad \text{(Eq. 4)}$$

After drying and weighing the three recovered compounds, you will calculate the percentage of each component in your unknown mixture. You will also calculate the percent recovery of the components of the mixture to determine the efficiency of your separation.

PROCEDURE

Chemical Alert

3*M* HCl—corrosive and toxic

CAUTION

Wear departmentally approved eye protection while doing this experiment.

I. Preparing the Mixture for Separation

1. Label two clean, dry 150-mL beakers as Beakers 1 and 2. Determine the mass of each beaker to the nearest centigram (0.01 g). Record these masses on your Data Sheet.

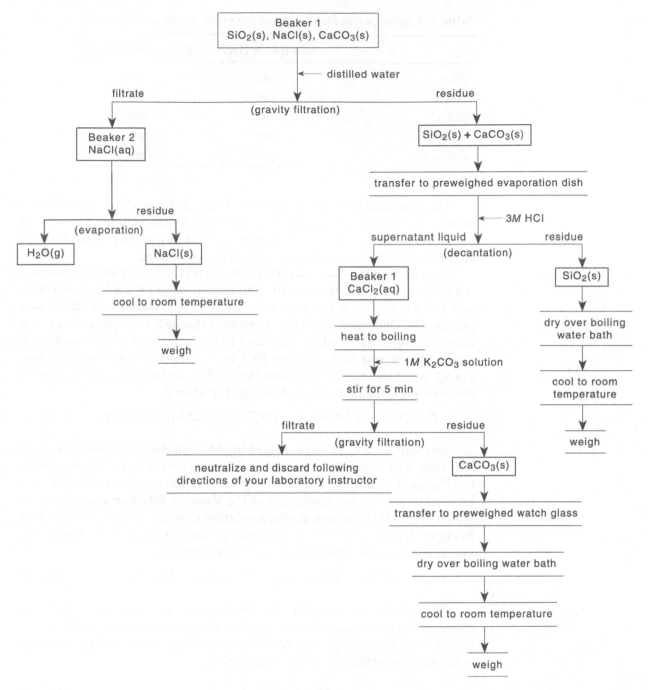

Figure 1
Flowchart for the separation of a mixture of SiO₂, NaCl, and CaCO₃

2. Obtain an unknown mixture of SiO_2, NaCl, and $CaCO_3$ from your laboratory instructor. Record the number of your unknown on your Data Sheet.

NOTE: The mass of your sample in Step 3 should be between 2.50 and 3.00 g.

---

3. Transfer a portion of your mixture to Beaker 1. Measure the mass of this sample and Beaker 1 to the nearest centigram (0.01 g). Record this mass on your Data Sheet.

II. Recovering NaCl

A. *Extracting the Mixture with Water*

4. Measure 50 mL of distilled or deionized water in a graduated cylinder. Slowly add the water to the mixture in Beaker 1 while continuously stirring with a clean, glass stirring rod. After completing the addition, stir the mixture for an additional 2-min period.

NOTE: Your laboratory instructor will inform you if you are to recover the NaCl by using gravity filtration, as described here, or vacuum filtration, as described in Part IV.

B. *Preparing the Funnel Assembly for Gravity Filtration*

5. Place a clean filtering funnel in a small iron ring, in a funnel stand, or in a utility clamp attached to a ring stand, as shown in Figure 2.

6. Begin by folding a piece of filter paper as shown in Figure 3. Fold the circle of filter paper exactly in half, as shown in Figure 3(b). Make a second fold, as shown in Figure 3(c), so that the edges of the filter paper do not quite match, as shown in Figure 3(d). Make certain that the angle formed by the two edges of the paper is between 5 and 10 degrees.

7. Tear off the corner of the smaller section of the filter paper, as shown in Figure 3(e). By tearing off the corner of the filter paper, you will form a tighter seal between the funnel and the paper during filtration. Open up the paper cone and place it in the funnel, as shown in Figure 3(f). Place the torn-off corner in the filter paper cone.

8. Place the second preweighed beaker, labeled Beaker 2, under the funnel. Make certain the stem of the funnel touches the side of the beaker. This arrangement minimizes splattering during filtration.

9. Moisten the filter paper in the funnel with distilled water from a wash bottle. Firmly press the edges of the filter paper against the funnel so that the paper adheres tightly to the funnel. This seal increases the

Figure 2
A gravity filtration assembly

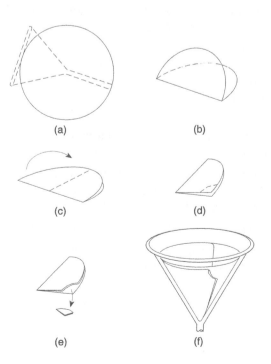

(a)   (b)

(c)   (d)

(e)   (f)

Figure 3
Folding a piece of filter paper

Figure 4

Transferring a supernatant liquid from a beaker to a filtering funnel

Figure 5

Transferring a solid from a beaker to a filtering funnel

filtration rate and prevents loss of product. Add to the funnel sufficient distilled water from a wash bottle to fill the stem of the funnel.

C. Filtering the Mixture

10. Decant as much of the supernatant liquid as possible into the funnel. To prevent splashing and loss of solid, use a clean, glass stirring rod to guide the liquid from Beaker 1 into the funnel, as shown in Figure 4. Collect the filtrate in Beaker 2.

11. Transfer the solid remaining in Beaker 1 to the funnel by using a stream of distilled water from the wash bottle, as shown in Figure 5. Transfer any remaining solid by using a stirring rod fitted with a rubber policeman.

12. After you have transferred the solid, position the stirring rod so that the attached rubber policeman is directly above the funnel. Direct a stream of distilled water from the wash bottle onto the policeman. Allow the washings to go into the funnel and drain into Beaker 2.

D. Evaporating the Filtrate

CAUTION

As the volume of the solution decreases in Step 13, the risk of splattering increases. Gentle heating and attentiveness will reduce this risk.

Avoid contact with any steam that might be produced during Step 13.

13. Place Beaker 2, containing the filtrate, on a hot plate set at a high setting. Heat the solution to boiling. Reduce the hot plate setting so the solution continues to boil gently until only about 10 mL remain. Adjust the hot plate to a lower setting and continue boiling the solution until only 2–3 mL remain. Adjust the hot plate to the lowest setting and continue heating the beaker and its contents until all of the liquid has evaporated. Turn off the hot plate.

CAUTION

Avoid burning your hands by preventing direct contact between your hands and the hot beaker.

Use beaker tongs, a strip of paper, or a towel to remove the beaker from the hot plate, as shown in Figure 6.

14. Allow the beaker and its contents to cool to room temperature. Determine the mass of Beaker 2 and its contents to the nearest centigram (0.01 g). Record this mass on your Data Sheet.

15. Discard the NaCl following the directions of your laboratory instructor.

16. Wash Beakers 1 and 2 and rinse each twice, using a 10-mL portion of distilled water for each rinse. Dry Beaker 1 for use in Part III.

III. Recovering SiO$_2$

A. Transferring the SiO$_2$/CaCO$_3$ Residue to an Evaporating Dish

17. Determine the mass of a clean, dry evaporating dish to the nearest centigram (0.01 g). Record this mass on your Data Sheet.

18. Use forceps to carefully remove the filter paper and the SiO$_2$/CaCO$_3$ residue from the funnel. Place the paper and residue in the preweighed evaporating dish. Use the forceps to open and hold the filter paper. Wash the residue from the filter paper into the evaporating dish with a stream of about 5 mL of distilled water from a wash bottle. Discard the filter paper.

B. Reacting the Residue with HCl

CAUTION

3M HCl is a corrosive, toxic substance that can cause burns. Prevent contact with your eyes, skin, and clothing. Avoid inhaling vapors.

NOTE: In Step 19, add the acid slowly to control the evolution of CO$_2$ gas, avoiding the sudden release of a large amount of gas. Such action could cause a loss of SiO$_2$ and CaCO$_3$.

19. Measure 8 mL of 3M HCl in a clean, dry graduated cylinder. Slowly add the acid to the residue. Stir the solution with a clean glass stirring rod until there is no evidence of gas evolution.

C. Decanting the Supernatant Liquid from the SiO$_2$

20. Decant as much of the supernatant liquid as possible from the evaporating dish into Beaker 1. Be sure that none of the SiO$_2$ is transferred to this beaker. Wash the SiO$_2$ remaining in the evaporating dish with a stream of about 5 mL of distilled water. Allow the solid to

Figure 6

Removing a hot beaker from a hot plate

settle to the bottom of the dish. Decant the washing into Beaker 1. Repeat the washing procedure twice, each time using 5 mL of distilled water. Each time, decant the washings into Beaker 1. Save the supernatant liquid and washings for use in Part IV.

D. Drying SiO₂

NOTE: Your laboratory instructor might prefer that you store the dish and the SiO₂ residue in your locker to dry until the next laboratory period.

CAUTION

Avoid burning your hands by preventing direct contact between your hand and the hot beaker or any steam coming from beneath the watch glass in Step 21.

---

21. Dry the SiO₂ by placing the evaporating dish on top of a beaker of boiling water on a hot plate, as shown in Figure 7 Before you begin to heat the water in the beaker, add to the water two glass beads or boiling stones to provide steady boiling without bumping. Heat the water to boiling and continue heating until the SiO₂ is completely dry. Use crucible tongs to remove the evaporating dish and its contents from on top of the beaker.

22. Allow the dish and its contents to cool to room temperature. Carefully dry the bottom of the dish with a clean towel. Determine the mass of the dish and its contents to the nearest centigram (0.01 g). Record the mass on your Data Sheet.

23. Discard your SiO₂ following the directions of your laboratory instructor.

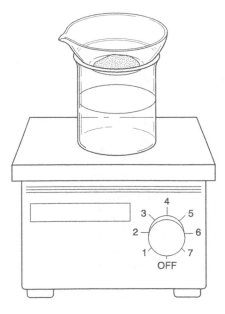

Figure 7

Drying a solid in an evaporating dish

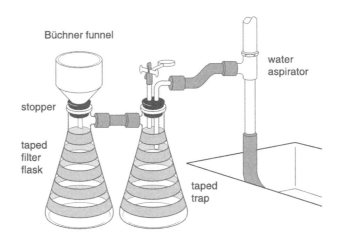

Figure 8
A vacuum filtration apparatus

IV. Recovering CaCO₃

A. Precipitating CaCO₃

24. Place Beaker 1, containing the supernatant liquid and washings from Part III, on a hot plate and heat to boiling. Allow the solution to boil for 5 min. Using crucible tongs, carefully remove Beaker 1 from the hot plate and immediately add 15 mL of $1M$ K_2CO_3 solution, measured in a graduated cylinder. Stir the reaction mixture for 5 min. Allow the mixture to cool to room temperature.

B. Preweighing Watch Glass and Filter Paper

25. Label a clean, dry watch glass with an identifying mark. Place a piece of filter paper on the watch glass. Weigh the watch glass and filter paper to the nearest centigram (0.01 g). Record this mass on your Data Sheet.

NOTE: Your laboratory instructor will inform you if you are to recover the $CaCO_3$ by using vacuum filtration, as described here, or gravity filtration, as described in Part II.

C. Preparing the Funnel Assembly for Vacuum Filtration

26. Assemble a vacuum filtration apparatus, as shown in Figure 8. Place the preweighed piece of filter paper in the Büchner funnel. To ensure an airtight seal between the filter paper and the funnel, moisten the filter paper with a small amount of distilled or deionized water.

27. Turn on the water aspirator. Take the pressure tubing attached to the aspirator and connect this tubing to the side arm of the filter flask.

28. Decant as much of the supernatant liquid in Beaker 1 as possible into the Büchner funnel. To prevent splashing and loss of precipitate, use a glass stirring rod to guide the liquid from the beaker onto the filter paper in the bottom of the Büchner funnel, as shown in Figure 9.

29. Complete the transfer of the $CaCO_3$ from the beaker to the funnel by using a stream of distilled water from the wash bottle, as shown in Figure 10. Wash as much of the $CaCO_3$ as possible from the beaker into the funnel. Transfer any remaining solid using a stirring rod fitted with a rubber policeman.

precipitate

Figure 9

Transferring a supernatant liquid from a beaker to a Büchner funnel

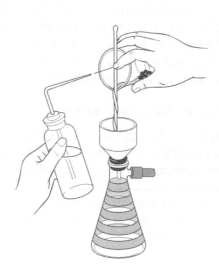

Figure 10

Washing a solid from a beaker into a Büchner funnel

NOTE: Be sure to disconnect the pressure tubing from the side arm of the flask *before* turning off the water aspirator.

---

30. After you have transferred the CaCO₃, position the stirring rod so that the attached rubber policeman is directly above the funnel. Direct a stream of distilled water from the wash bottle onto the policeman. Allow the washings to go into the funnel. Draw air through the funnel for 5 min. Disconnect the pressure tubing from the side arm of the flask. Turn off the water aspirator.

31. Discard the filtrate in the bottom of the filter flask following the directions of your laboratory instructor.

D. Drying CaCO₃

NOTE: Your laboratory instructor might prefer that you store the CaCO₃, filter paper, and watch glass in your locker to dry until the next laboratory period.

---

32. Carefully remove the filter paper and $CaCO_3$ from the Büchner funnel. Place the paper and solid on the preweighed watch glass. Dry the $CaCO_3$ and paper by placing the watch glass and solid over a beaker of boiling water containing two glass beads or boiling stones on a hot plate. (See Figure 7.) Continue the heating until the filter paper and $CaCO_3$ are completely dry. Use crucible tongs to remove the watch glass, filter paper, and its contents from the top of the beaker.

33. Allow the watch glass, filter paper, and $CaCO_3$ residue to cool to room temperature. Carefully dry the bottom of the watch glass. Determine the mass of the watch glass and its contents to the nearest centigram (0.01 g). Record this mass on your Data Sheet.

34. Discard your $CaCO_3$ following the directions of your laboratory instructor.

V. Doing a Second Determination

35. If time permits, do a second determination. Wash both beakers and rinse each twice using a 10-mL portion of distilled water for each rinse. Dry the beakers for use during the second determination.

36. Repeat Steps 1 and 3–34, using a second portion of your unknown sample.

CAUTION

Wash your hands thoroughly with soap or detergent before leaving the laboratory.

CALCULATIONS

Do the following calculations for each determination and record the results on your Data Sheet.

1. Calculate the mass of the sample of your unknown mixture.
2. Calculate the mass of NaCl recovered.
3. Calculate the mass of SiO_2 recovered.
4. Calculate the mass of $CaCO_3$ recovered.
5. Calculate the percent NaCl in your unknown mixture, using Equation 5.

$$\text{percent NaCl in the mixture} = \left(\frac{\text{mass of NaCl recovered, g}}{\text{mass of sample, g}} \right)(100\%)$$

(Eq. 5)

6. Calculate the percent SiO_2 in your mixture.
7. Calculate the percent $CaCO_3$ in your mixture.
8. Calculate the percent recovery of the components, using Equation 6.

$$\text{percent recovery} = \left(\frac{\text{total mass of recovered components}}{\text{mass of sample, g}} \right)(100\%)$$

(Eq. 6)

9. Calculate the percent error for the separation of your mixture, using Equation 7.

$$percent\ error = \left(\frac{\begin{array}{c} \text{mass of original} \\ \text{sample, g} \end{array} - \begin{array}{c} \text{total mass of recovered} \\ \text{components, g} \end{array}}{\text{mass of original sample, g}} \right)(100\%)$$

(Eq. 7)

10. Calculate the mean percent error for Determinations 1 and 2, using Equation 8.

$$mean\ percent\ error = \left(\frac{\begin{array}{c} \text{percent error for} \\ \text{Determination 1} \end{array} + \begin{array}{c} \text{percent error for} \\ \text{Determination 2} \end{array}}{2} \right)$$

(Eq. 8)

_____   _____   _____
name   *section*   *date*

Post-Laboratory Questions

(Use the spaces provided for the answers and additional paper if necessary.)

1. List possible manipulation errors that might contribute to the following errors in results:

(1) obtaining a significantly larger amount of NaCl than was present in the original sample;

(2) obtaining a significantly smaller amount of SiO_2 than was present in the original sample.

2. Use the information in the table to answer the following questions.

	Soluble in:			
	cold water	*hot water*	*3M HCl*	*3M NaOH*
benzoic acid	no	yes	no	yes
$Mg(OH)_2$	no	no	yes	no
Na_2SO_4	yes	yes	yes	yes
$Zn(OH)_2$	no	no	yes	yes

(1) Could you separate the components of a mixture of $Mg(OH)_2$ and $Zn(OH)_2$ by using 3M HCl? Briefly explain your answer.

(2) Briefly describe how you could separate the components of a mixture of benzoic acid and Na_2SO_4 and recover the two separated substances.

(3) Could you separate the components of a mixture of benzoic acid, $Mg(OH)_2$, and Na_2SO_4 by using only cold water and $3M$ HCl? Briefly explain your answer.

(4) A mixture was known to contain three of the four compounds in the table. After the mixture of the three solids was extracted with hot water and filtered, Compound A was obtained by evaporating the filtrate to dryness.

When $3M$ HCl was added to the solid residue, a clear solution resulted. After adding excess $3M$ NaOH solution to the acid solution, a precipitate formed. After filtration, the insoluble solid was found to be Compound B. Compound C was recovered by evaporation of the filtrate. Neither Compound A, B, nor C was soluble in all of the solvents, that is water, $3M$ HCl, and $3M$ NaOH.

Identify Compounds A, B, and C. Briefly explain your answer.

_____   _____   _____
name   *section*   *date*

Data Sheet

code number of unknown mixture _____

	determination	
	first	*second*
mass of Beaker 1 + sample, g	_____	_____
mass of Beaker 1, g	_____	_____
mass of sample, g	_____	_____
mass of Beaker 2 + NaCl, g	_____	_____
mass of Beaker 2, g	_____	_____
mass of NaCl, g	_____	_____
mass of evaporating dish + SiO_2, g	_____	_____
mass of evaporating dish, g	_____	_____
mass of SiO_2, g	_____	_____
mass of watch glass, filter paper + $CaCO_3$, g	_____	_____
mass of watch glass + filter paper, g	_____	_____
mass of $CaCO_3$, g	_____	_____
total mass of recovered NaCl, SiO_2, and $CaCO_3$, g	_____	_____
percent NaCl in the mixture	_____	_____
percent SiO_2 in the mixture	_____	_____
percent $CaCO_3$ in the mixture	_____	_____
percent recovery	_____	_____
percent error	_____	_____
mean percent error	_____	

name   section   date

Pre-Laboratory Assignment

1. Read an authoritative source for a discussion of filtration.

2. What precautions should you take when handling $3M$ HCl and $1M$ K_2CO_3 solutions?

3. Define the following terms.
  (1) heterogeneous mixture

  (2) evaporation

  (3) supernatant liquid

4. Why should you be careful when you heat your NaCl solution to evaporate the water?

5. A student was asked to determine the percentage of the components of a mixture of potassium bromide (KBr), magnesium hydroxide, $Mg(OH)_2$, and barium sulfate ($BaSO_4$). The mass of the sample of the mixture used was 3.21 g.

   The student extracted the KBr from the mixture with water and filtered insoluble $Mg(OH)_2$ and $BaSO_4$ from the solution, containing the KBr. After evaporating the filtrate, the student recovered and dried the KBr and found it weighed 1.43 g.

   The student treated the insoluble residue of $Mg(OH)_2$ and $BaSO_4$ with $3M$ HCl, dissolving the $Mg(OH)_2$. The student then decanted the supernatant liquid containing aqueous $MgCl_2$ from the insoluble $BaSO_4$. After drying the solid, the student recovered 0.58 g of $BaSO_4$.

The student next added $3M$ KOH solution to the aqueous solution, and $Mg(OH)_2$ precipitated. After filtering the solution and drying the precipitate, the student recovered 1.10 g of $Mg(OH)_2$.

(1) On the basis of the mass of sample used:

    (a) Calculate the percent KBr in the mixture;

    (b) Calculate the percent $Mg(OH)_2$ in the mixture;

    (c) Calculate the percent $BaSO_4$ in the mixture.

(2) Write a chemical equation for the reaction of solid $Mg(OH)_2$ and aqueous HCl.

(3) Calculate the percent recovery, using the total mass of substances recovered.

(4) Calculate the percent error for the separation of the components of the mixture.

6. A mixture of NaCl, SiO_2, and $CaCO_3$ is separated following the procedure given in this experiment. Indicate how each of the following procedural changes would affect the amount of the specified substance recovered. Briefly explain.

(1) The recovery of $CaCO_3$ was attempted by adding $3M$ H_2SO_4 instead of $3M$ HCl to the SiO_2/$CaCO_3$ residue.

(2) The recovery of $CaCO_3$ was attempted by adding $1M$ KNO_3 solution instead of $1M$ K_2CO_3 solution to the filtrate, containing aqueous $CaCl_2$.

PROP0375: Separating the Components of a Ternary Mixture

Single Replacement Reactions and Relative Reactivity

Prepared by H. A. Neidig, Lebanon Valley College, and
J. N. Spencer, Franklin and Marshall College

PURPOSE OF THE EXPERIMENT

Determine the relative reactivity of aluminum, iron, and copper.

BACKGROUND INFORMATION

A chemical change alters a substance or substances, forming new substances. Collisions between molecules and between ions that produce chemical reactions result in chemical changes. In some reactions, called **single replacement reactions**, one element displaces another.

We represent a single replacement reaction by the general equation

$$A + BC \rightarrow B + AC \qquad \text{(Eq. 1)}$$

where A, a metal, and BC, an ionic compound of a metal (B) and a nonmetal (C), react to form B, now a free metal, and AC, an ionic compound. The process involves the transfer of electrons from A to B.

In this type of reaction, a competition exists between the two elements. One element loses an electron (or electrons) to another element that is less able to lose electrons. Or, one element takes an electron (or electrons) from another element less able to take electrons.

We can write the general equation for single replacement reactions another way. Often, we wish to recognize the state of the reactants and products. In order to do this, we use the notation (s) for a solid, (*l*) for a liquid, (g) for a gas, and (aq) for a substance dissolved in water. If, in Equation 1, A and B are solids and BC and AC are substances dissolved in water, then Equation 1 may be written:

$$A(s) + BC(aq) \rightarrow B(s) + AC(aq) \qquad \text{(Eq. 2)}$$

The first type of single replacement reaction we will consider involves a metal A and a solution of a strong acid BC. If we place zinc (Zn), a bluish–white metal, in aqueous hydrochloric acid (HCl), a strong acid, a colorless solution of zinc chloride ($ZnCl_2$) and bubbles of colorless hydrogen gas (H_2) form. We observe H_2 bubbles moving up and out of the solution while the surface of the Zn changes. If we use excess aqueous HCl, all of the Zn will dissolve. Equation 3 represents this reaction.

$$Zn(s, \text{bluish-white}) + 2\,HCl(aq) \rightarrow ZnCl_2(aq) + H_2(g) \qquad (\text{Eq. 3})$$

In this reaction, Zn metal loses electrons and hydrogen ions (H^+) gain electrons to form H_2. The reverse of this reaction, shown in Equation 4, does not occur.

$$ZnCl_2(aq) + H_2(g) \rightarrow \text{no reaction} \qquad (\text{Eq. 4})$$

Thus, we say that Zn metal is more *active* than H_2 because Zn metal loses electrons more easily than H_2 does. If a metal is less active than H_2, no reaction will occur when the metal is added to a strong acid.

Evidence of a reaction will be the formation and release of H_2 bubbles and a change in the appearance of the metal as it reacts and goes into solution. Reactive metals will react with aqueous HCl at different rates, with some of these metals showing a rapid release of H_2 and others a very slow release.

Equation 3 can be written as a **total ionic equation** where all aqueous substances are assumed to have dissociated into ions in the solution. Because aqueous HCl is a strong acid, it is highly dissociated in water, forming hydronium ion (H_3O^+) and chloride ion (Cl^-), as shown by Equation 5. Note that the ions are hydrated in solution and written as $H_3O^+(aq)$ and $Cl^-(aq)$.

$$HCl(aq) + H_2O(l) \rightarrow H_3O^+(aq) + Cl^-(aq) \qquad (\text{Eq. 5})$$

Thus, the HCl(aq) in Equation 3 is written as $H_3O^+(aq) + Cl^-$ (aq) in the total ionic equation, as shown in Equation 7.

Solid zinc chloride is a white metallic salt that becomes highly dissociated when dissolved in water. This process is referred to as **dissolution** and is represented by Equation 6.

$$ZnCl_2(aq) \rightarrow Zn^{2+}(aq) + 2\,Cl^-(aq) \qquad (\text{Eq. 6})$$

The total ionic equation for the reaction of Zn and aqueous HCl is shown in Equation 7.

$$Zn(s, \text{bluish-white}) + 2\,H_3O^+(aq) + 2\,Cl^-(aq) \rightarrow Zn^{2+}(aq) + 2\,Cl^-(aq) + H_2(g) + 2\,H_2O(l) \qquad (\text{Eq. 7})$$

We note that in Equation 7, Cl^- ion appears in equal amounts as reactant and product. Because the Cl^- ion does not change during the reaction, we can cancel these ions from both sides of the equation. In such cases, these ions are referred to as **spectator ions**. The resulting Equation 8 shows only those species involved in the reaction and is the **net ionic equation** for the reaction.

$$Zn(s, \text{bluish-white}) + 2\,H_3O^+(aq) \rightarrow Zn^{2+}(aq) + H_2(g) + 2\,H_2O(l) \qquad (\text{Eq. 8})$$

A second type of single replacement reaction involves a metal and a solution of a metallic salt. If we place reddish metallic copper (Cu) in a colorless silver nitrate solution ($AgNO_3$), the reaction in Equation 9 occurs. The products in this reaction are blue copper(II) nitrate solution, $Cu(NO_3)_2$, and white metallic silver (Ag).

$$Cu(s, reddish) + 2\,AgNO_3(aq) \rightarrow Cu(NO_3)_2(aq,\ blue) + 2\,Ag(s,\ white) \qquad (Eq.\ 9)$$

In this reaction, Cu metal loses electrons and Ag^+ ions gain electrons. The reverse of this reaction, as shown in Equation 10, does not occur.

$$2\,Ag(s,\ white) + Cu(NO_3)_2(aq,\ blue) \rightarrow no\ reaction \qquad (Eq.\ 10)$$

Thus, we say that Cu metal is more active than Ag metal because Cu metal loses electrons more easily than Ag metal does. Note that Equation 9 is written with all substances in their undissociated form.

The total ionic equation for the reaction shown in Equation 9 is given in Equation 11.

$$Cu(s, reddish) + 2\,Ag^+(aq) + 2\,NO_3^-(aq) \rightarrow Cu^{2+}(aq,\ blue) + 2\,NO_3^-(aq) + 2\,Ag(s,\ white) \qquad (Eq.\ 11)$$

By eliminating the spectator nitrate ion (NO_3^-) on both sides of Equation 11, we obtain the net ionic equation for the reaction, Equation 12.

$$Cu(s, reddish) + 2\,Ag^+(aq) \rightarrow Cu^{2+}(aq,\ blue) + 2\,Ag(s,\ white) \qquad (Eq.\ 12)$$

If we place Cu metal in colorless zinc sulfate solution ($ZnSO_4$), no reaction is observed.

$$Cu(s, reddish) + ZnSO_4(aq) \rightarrow no\ reaction \qquad (Eq.\ 13)$$

Therefore, when comparing the reactivity of Cu metal and Zn metal with respect to their ability to lose electrons, Zn metal is more active. We can confirm this conclusion by placing excess bluish-white Zn metal in a blue copper(II) sulfate solution ($CuSO_4$). The single replacement reaction shown in the net ionic equation, Equation 14, occurs.

$$Zn(s, bluish\text{-}white) + Cu^{2+}(aq,\ blue) \rightarrow Zn^{2+}(aq) + Cu(s,\ reddish) \qquad (Eq.\ 14)$$

Reddish metallic Cu is deposited on the bottom of the reaction vessel, and the solution becomes colorless. Usually the surface of any remaining Zn metal will indicate also that a reaction has occurred.

The formation of H_2 bubbles when a metal is added to a strong acid indicates that a reaction is occurring. However, the evolution of H_2 when a metal is added to a metallic salt solution does not indicate that the metal is replacing the metallic ion of the metallic salt.

If the metallic salt solution is sufficiently acidic to react with the metal, H_2 will also be produced. Both reactions can occur at the same time, as indicated by the formation of H_2 gas and the deposition of a different metal or a change in the color of the metallic solution. If we observe only the appearance of H_2 and the disappearance of some or all of the original metal, then we cannot say that one metal is more active than another.

Another type of single replacement can occur when an element that attracts an electron very strongly replaces a negatively charged species in a compound. For example, when we add slightly yellow chlorine water, $Cl_2(aq)$, to a colorless sodium bromide solution (NaBr), the reaction in Equation 15 occurs.

$$Cl_2(aq, \text{ slightly yellow}) + 2\,NaBr(aq) \rightleftharpoons 2\,NaCl(aq) + Br_2(l, \text{ dark red}) \qquad \text{(Eq. 15)}$$

The net ionic equation for Equation 16 is

$$Cl_2(aq, \text{ slightly yellow}) + 2\,Br^-(aq) \rightleftharpoons 2\,Cl^-(aq) + Br_2(l, \text{ dark red}) \qquad \text{(Eq. 16)}$$

In this reaction, Cl_2 gains electrons more easily than Br_2 and replaces the bromide ion (Br^-) in the compound.

The **relative reactivity** of one element to another can be established in the laboratory. We can determine this order by observing whether or not a chemical reaction occurs when two substances are mixed. For example, from a series of experiments investigators have found the order of increasing reactivity for the halogens to be

$$\underrightarrow{\quad I_2 < Br_2 < Cl_2 < F_2 \quad}$$
increasing ease of gaining electrons

Thus, chlorine (Cl_2) will replace bromide ion (Br^-) in a single replacement reaction, but chlorine (Cl_2) will not replace fluoride ion (F^-).

In this experiment, you will establish a relative reactivity series for aluminum (Al), iron (Fe), copper (Cu), and hydrogen (H_2). You will determine the order from observations of chemical changes occurring when single replacement reactions of these metals and their metallic ions are carried out. You will also consider the reactions of the metals with aqueous HCl.

PROCEDURE

CHEMICAL ALERT

0.5*M* copper(II) sulfate—toxic and irritant
6*M* hydrochloric acid—toxic and corrosive
0.5*M* iron(II) sulfate—toxic

CAUTION

Wear departmentally approved eye protection while doing this experiment.

NOTE: The numbers appearing in parentheses indicate the lines on your Data Sheet on which the indicated data should be entered.

I. Observing the Appearance of Metals and Solutions of Their Metallic Salts

1. Examine samples of Al, Cu, and Fe. Record on Data Sheet 1 (1) characteristics of the metals such as color, texture, and luster.

CAUTION

$6M$ HCl is a corrosive, toxic substance that can cause burns. Avoid contact with your eyes, skin, and clothing. Avoid inhaling vapors and ingesting the compound.

2. Examine solutions of aluminum sulfate, $Al_2(SO_4)_3$, $CuSO_4$, aqueous HCl, and iron(II) sulfate ($FeSO_4$). Record on Data Sheet 1 (2) characteristics of these solutions such as color.

II. Reacting Metals with Dilute Hydrochloric Acid

3. Obtain three 4-cm pieces each of Al wire, Cu wire, and Fe wire. Clean each piece of metal with sandpaper to remove any metallic oxide and to expose the metal surface.

4. In a clean 10-mL graduated cylinder, measure 9 mL of $6M$ HCl. Pour 3 mL of $6M$ HCl into each of three clean test tubes.

NOTE: For each of the following steps, observe the reaction mixture for 5 min before recording any observations on Data Sheet 2.

NOTE: In some parts of this experiment, a reaction will not occur. When this is the case, write "no reaction" in the appropriate space under the heading "*chemical equation*" on Data Sheet 2.

NOTE: Your laboratory instructor will inform you as to what type of chemical equation you should write; i.e., total ionic or net ionic equation.

5. Carefully place a 4-cm piece of Al wire in one test tube containing aqueous HCl. Record your observations on Data Sheet 2 (3). If a chemical reaction occurs, write a chemical equation on Data Sheet 2 (4) for the reaction.

6. Carefully place a 4-cm piece of Cu wire in a second test tube containing aqueous HCl. Record your observations on Data Sheet 2 (5). If appropriate, write a chemical equation on Data Sheet 2 (6) for the reaction.

7. Carefully place a 4-cm piece of Fe wire in the third test tube containing aqueous HCl. Record your observations on Data Sheet 2 (7). If appropriate, write a chemical equation on Data Sheet 2 (8) for the reaction.

8. Discard the acid solutions and any unreacted metal into the containers specified by your laboratory instructor and labelled, "*Discarded Al Reaction Mixtures,*" "*Discarded Cu Reaction Mixtures,*" and "*Discarded Fe Reaction Mixtures.*"

9. Thoroughly wash the graduated cylinder and the three test tubes. Rinse them three times with tap water, and then three times with distilled or deionized water.

III. Reacting Metals with Solutions of Metallic Salts

10. Obtain about 6 mL of $0.5M$ $Al_2(SO_4)_3$ solution in a clean 10-mL graduated cylinder. Pour 3 mL of $Al_2(SO_4)_3$ solution into each of two clean test tubes.

NOTE: For each of the following steps, observe the reaction mixture for 5 min before recording any observations on Data Sheet 3.

---

11. Carefully place a 4-cm piece of Cu wire in one of the test tubes containing $Al_2(SO_4)_3$ solution. Record your observations on Data Sheet 3 (9). If appropriate, write a chemical equation on Data Sheet 3 (10) for the reaction.

12. Carefully place a 4-cm piece of Fe wire in the second test tube containing $Al_2(SO_4)_3$ solution. Record your observations on Data Sheet 3 (11). If appropriate, write a chemical equation on Data Sheet 3 (12) for the reaction.

13. Discard the solutions and unreacted metal into the containers specified by your laboratory instructor and labelled, *"Discarded Cu—$Al_2(SO_4)_3$ Reaction Mixtures,"* and *"Discarded Fe—$Al_2(SO_4)_3$ Reaction Mixtures."*

14. Thoroughly wash the graduated cylinder and the two test tubes. Rinse them three times with tap water, and then three times with distilled or deionized water.

15. Obtain about 6 mL of $0.5M$ $FeSO_4$ solution in a clean 10-mL graduated cylinder. Pour 3 mL of the $FeSO_4$ solution into each of two clean test tubes.

16. Carefully place a 4-cm piece of Al wire in one of the test tubes containing $FeSO_4$ solution. Record your observations on Data Sheet 3 (13). If appropriate, write a chemical equation on Data Sheet 3 (14) for the reaction.

17. Carefully place a 4-cm piece of Cu wire in the second test tube containing $FeSO_4$ solution. Record your observations on Data Sheet 3 (15). If appropriate, write a chemical equation on Data Sheet 3 (16) for the reaction.

18. Discard the solutions and unreacted metal into the containers specified by your laboratory instructor and labelled, *"Discarded Al—$FeSO_4$ Reaction Mixtures,"* and *"Discarded Cu—$FeSO_4$ Reaction Mixtures."*

19. Thoroughly wash the graduated cylinder and the two test tubes. Rinse them three times with tap water, and then three times with distilled or deionized water.

20. Obtain about 6 mL of $0.5M$ $CuSO_4$ solution in a clean 10-mL graduated cylinder. Pour 3 mL of the $CuSO_4$ solution into each of two clean test tubes.

21. Carefully place a 4-cm piece of Al wire in one of the clean test tubes containing $CuSO_4$ solution. Record your observations on Data Sheet 3 (17). If appropriate, write a chemical equation on Data Sheet 3 (18) for the reaction.

22. Carefully place a 4-cm piece of Fe wire in the second test tube containing $CuSO_4$ solution. Record your observations on Data Sheet 3 (19). If appropriate, write a chemical equation on Data Sheet 3 (20) for the reaction.

23. Discard the solutions and unreacted metal into the containers specified by your laboratory instructor and labelled, *"Discarded Al—CuSO₄ Reaction Mixtures,"* and *"Discarded Fe—CuSO₄ Reaction Mixtures."*

24. Thoroughly wash the graduated cylinder and the two test tubes. Rinse them three times with tap water, and then three times with distilled or deionized water.

IV. Considering Your Observations and Equations

25. Arrange the three metals and H_2 in order of increasing relative reactivity. Record this order on Data Sheet 4 (21).

26. Summarize on Data Sheet 4 (22) the chemical evidence you obtained to justify your reactivity series.

Name _____ Section _____ Date _____

Post-Laboratory Questions

1. **(1)** Explain why it was important to clean each piece of metal you used with sandpaper prior to doing the experiment.

   (2) What specific problem might you have encountered had you cleaned the metal surfaces with a soft tissue instead?

2. On the basis of your results from this experiment, what observation(s) did you make that would allow you to determine the place H_2 would take in your relative activity series?

3. (1) Write a total ionic equation for the reaction (if any) of $FeCl_2$ solution with Cu, and for the reaction (if any) of $FeCl_2$ solution with Al.

(2) Write a net ionic equation for the reaction(s) in 3 (1).

(3) Briefly explain why you would or would not have obtained the same experimental results if $FeCl_2$ solution had been used instead of $FeSO_4$ solution in Steps 16 and 17 of the experiment described in this module.

Name   *Section*   *Date*

Data Sheet 1

I. Observing the Appearance of Metals and Solutions of Their Metallic Salts

metal   *appearance*

Al   **(1)**

Cu

Fe

metallic salt solutions   *appearance*

$Al_2(SO_4)_3$ **(2)**

$CuSO_4$

HCl

$FeSO_4$

Name	*Section*	*Date*

Data Sheet 2

II. Reacting Metals with Dilute Hydrochloric Acid

metal	*observations*	*chemical equation*
Al	**(3)**	**(4)**
Cu	**(5)**	**(6)**
Fe	**(7)**	**(8)**

Name   Section   Date

Data Sheet 3

III. Reacting Metals with Solutions of Metallic Salts

metal	solution of metallic salt		observations		chemical equation
Cu	$Al_2(SO_4)_3$	(9)		(10)	
Fe	$Al_2(SO_4)_3$	(11)		(12)	
Al	$FeSO_4$	(13)		(14)	
Cu	$FeSO_4$	(15)		(16)	
Al	$CuSO_4$	(17)		(18)	
Fe	$CuSO_4$	(19)		(20)	

Name _____   Section _____   Date _____

Data Sheet 4

IV. Considering Your Observations and Equations

(21) Arrange the three metals and hydrogen in order of their increasing relative reactivity:

_____ < _____ < _____ < _____
     least reactive   most reactive

(22) The justification for this order of increasing relative reactivity is

Name _____   Section _____   Date _____

Pre-Laboratory Assignment

1. **(1)** Explain why it is important to be especially careful while pouring $6M$ HCl into your graduated cylinder and test tubes in Part II of this experiment.

   (2) What should you do if some M HCl drips down the outside of your graduated cylinder while you are filling the cylinder?

2. Zinc (Zn) metal is more active than tin (Sn) metal.

   (1) Would a reaction occur if a zinc sulfate solution ($ZnSO_4$) and a tin(II) sulfate solution ($SnSO_4$) were mixed? Briefly explain your answer. Write a net ionic equation if a reaction does occur.

(2) Would a reaction occur if a piece of metallic Sn were placed in distilled water with a piece of metallic Zn? Briefly explain your answer. Write a net ionic equation if a reaction does occur.

(3) Would a reaction occur if a piece of Zn metal were placed in a $SnSO_4$ solution? Briefly explain your answer. Write a net ionic equation if a reaction does occur.

(4) Would a reaction occur if a piece of Sn metal were placed in a $ZnSO_4$ solution? Briefly explain your answer. Write a net ionic equation if a reaction does occur.

3. A student did experiments to establish the relative reactivity of metallic Zn, Cu, and Pb. The following observations were made: (a) both Zn and Pb metals reacted with 6*M* HCl, but Cu metal did not; (b) there was no reaction between lead(II) sulfate solution ($PbSO_4$) and Cu metal, but there was a reaction between $PbSO_4$ solution and Zn metal.

(1) Write chemical equations based on each of the observations in (a) above.

(2) Write chemical equations describing the observations in (b).

(3) List the three metals and hydrogen in order of relative reactivity.

Reacting Vinegar with Baking Soda

Prepared by Henry D. Schreiber, Virginia Military Institute

PURPOSE OF THE EXPERIMENT

Use the reaction of household vinegar with baking soda to determine the mass percent acetic acid in the vinegar.

BACKGROUND INFORMATION

Reacting Acetic Acid and Sodium Bicarbonate

Question: What do a grocery store and a chemistry laboratory have in common? Answer: They are both places you can find chemicals. For example, baking soda purchased from a grocery store is identical to laboratory grade sodium bicarbonate, $NaHCO_3$. Similarly, household vinegar is a dilute aqueous solution of acetic acid, $HC_2H_3O_2$, a common laboratory chemical.

Mixing baking soda and vinegar results in a characteristic chemical reaction, the decomposition of sodium bicarbonate by acetic acid, as shown in Equation 1:

$$NaHCO_3(s) + HC_2H_3O_2(aq) \rightarrow Na^+(aq) + C_2H_3O_2^-(aq) + H_2O(l) + CO_2(g) \qquad \text{(Eq. 1)}$$

The hydrogen ion, H^+, from $HC_2H_3O_2$ combines with the bicarbonate ion, HCO_3^-, from baking soda to form water and carbon dioxide, CO_2. This reaction is analogous to one that occurs when unleavened (non-yeasted) breads and cakes bake, in which an acid in the dough or batter reacts with baking soda to liberate CO_2 gas. CO_2 bubbles released from the aqueous solution indicate that the reaction is still occurring. CO_2 generation continues until at least one of the reactants is consumed. As the CO_2 gas expands, the dough (or batter) rises.

Equation 1 shows that 1 mol of $NaHCO_3$ reacts with 1 mol of $HC_2H_3O_2$. Because the molar masses of $NaHCO_3$ and $HC_2H_3O_2$ are 84 g/mol and 60 g/mol, respectively, Equation 1 also indicates that 84 g of $NaHCO_3$ react completely with 60 g of $HC_2H_3O_2$. Such mathematical relationships among the reactants and products in a chemical equation are called the **stoichiometry** of the reaction. For example, if we start the reaction in Equation 1 with a known mass of $NaHCO_3$, the stoichiometry of the equation specifies the mass of $HC_2H_3O_2$ needed for complete reaction of the $NaHCO_3$. If excess $HC_2H_3O_2$ is present, the additional $HC_2H_3O_2$ will not react.

The objective in this experiment is to use the stoichiometry of Equation 1 to determine the concentration of acetic acid in household vinegar. Although baking soda is pure $NaHCO_3$, only a portion of the household vinegar is $HC_2H_3O_2$; the rest is mostly water. We start by measuring the volume of vinegar needed to completely react a known mass of $NaHCO_3$. When CO_2 stops bubbling from the reaction mixture, we know that we have added sufficient vinegar. Using the added vinegar volume, the original mass of $NaHCO_3$, and the stoichiometry of Equation 1, we can determine the concentration of acetic acid in the vinegar.

Illustrating the Experimental Approach and Required Calculations

Using a reaction similar to the one described by Equation 1, we can employ stoichiometry to determine the acetic acid concentration of vinegar. Potassium bicarbonate, $KHCO_3$, has properties similar to those of $NaHCO_3$. Like $NaHCO_3$, $KHCO_3$ is used in cooking, although only in low-moisture baked goods such as cookies and crackers. Also, like $NaHCO_3$, $KHCO_3$ reacts with acetic acid to produce water and CO_2 gas, as shown in Equation 2:

$$KHCO_3(s) + HC_2H_3O_2(aq) \rightarrow K^+(aq) + C_2H_3O_2^-(aq) + H_2O(l) + CO_2(g) \qquad \text{(Eq. 2)}$$

We can use the stoichiometry of Equation 2 to determine the mass percent of acetic acid in commercial-grade vinegar. **Mass percent** is the ratio between the mass of a component species present in one unit of a substance and the mass per unit of the substance, all multiplied by 100%. Typical commercial-grade vinegar is 10–13 mass percent acetic acid, which is much more concentrated than household vinegar.

We can use a series of $KHCO_3$–vinegar reactions to determine the volume of commercial-grade vinegar required to completely react with a specific mass of $KHCO_3$. Starting with a known mass of $KHCO_3$, we add commercial-grade vinegar until no more CO_2 evolves. At this point, we know that we have added sufficient vinegar to completely react the $KHCO_3$. Table 1 summarizes experimental data for four such determinations, using various $KHCO_3$ masses.

Using the data in Table 1, we can construct the straight line graph shown in Figure 1. The graph illustrates the relationship between commercialgrade vinegar volume in milliliters (plotted on the x-axis) and $KHCO_3$ mass in grams (plotted on the y-axis). The graph proves that in order to completely react both reagents, an increase in the amount of one reactant requires a fixed proportional increase in the amount of the other reactant. In addition, we know that the line must pass through the origin (0,0) because, if no $KHCO_3$ is present, no vinegar is required for reaction.

Table 1 *Data for four determinations involving complete reactions of commercial-grade vinegar and $KHCO_3$*

determination	$KHCO_3$, g	commercial-grade vinegar, mL
1	1.92	11
2	3.02	16
3	3.98	22
4	5.10	27

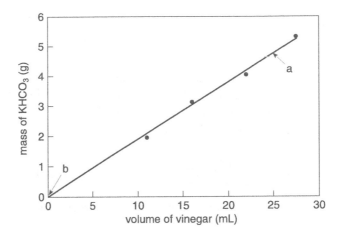

Figure 1

Relationship of mass of KHCO₃ to volume of commercial-grade vinegar required for complete reaction

We can determine the slope of the straight line in Figure 1 by choosing two points on the line, then dividing the difference in the y values of the two points by the difference in the x values of the points. For convenience, we can choose the origin as one of the two points. Suppose we choose points a ($x = 25$ mL, $y = 4.75$ g) and b (the origin, $x = 0$ mL, $y = 0$ g). We can then divide the difference in y values (4.75 g − 0 g = 4.75 g) by the difference in x values (25 mL − 0 mL = 25 mL) to obtain the slope of the line:

$$\text{slope} = \frac{(4.75 - 0)\,\text{g}}{(25 - 0)\,\text{mL}} = \frac{4.75\,\text{g KHCO}_3}{25\,\text{mL vinegar}} = 0.19\,\text{g KHCO}_3/\text{mL vinegar} \qquad \text{(Eq. 3)}$$

Alternately, we can determine the slope of the line using a computer spreadsheet program or scientific calculator to do a regression analysis of the experimental data.

Based on the stoichiometry of Equation 2, we can use Equation 4 to convert grams of KHCO₃ per milliliter of commercial-grade vinegar, the slope of the line in Figure 1, to grams of HC₂H₃O₂ per milliliter of commercial-grade vinegar.

$$\left(\frac{0.19\ \text{g KHCO}_3}{1\ \text{mL vinegar}}\right)\left(\frac{1\ \text{mol KHCO}_3}{100.1\ \text{g KHCO}_3}\right)\left(\frac{1\ \text{mol HC}_2\text{H}_3\text{O}_2}{1\ \text{mol KHCO}_3}\right)\left(\frac{60.0\ \text{g HC}_2\text{H}_3\text{O}_2}{1\ \text{mol HC}_2\text{H}_3\text{O}_2}\right)$$

$$= 0.11\ \text{g HC}_2\text{H}_3\text{O}_2/\text{mL commercial-grade vinegar} \qquad \text{(Eq. 4)}$$

In Equation 4, the first conversion factor is based on the molar mass of KHCO₃. The second factor is derived from the stoichiometry of Equation 2. The third factor is based on the molar mass of HC₂H₃O₂. We use the stoichiometry of Equation 2 to determine the ratio of the number of moles of each reactant needed for the complete reaction. We then use this ratio to relate the known mass of one reactant (KHCO₃, in this example) to the mass of the other reactant (HC₂H₃O₂).

Suppose that, in a separate procedure, we found that the mass of 25.0 mL of the commercial-grade vinegar was 25.4 g. We can calculate the vinegar's density by dividing sample mass by sample volume, as shown in Equation 5 on the next page.

$$\text{density of vinegar} = \frac{25.4 \text{ g}}{25.0 \text{ mL}} = 1.02 \text{ g/ml vinegar} \qquad \text{(Eq. 5)}$$

Once we know the density of the vinegar, we can determine the mass percent acetic acid in the commercial-grade vinegar by dividing the result of Equation 4 by the result of Equation 5, then multiplying by 100%, as shown in Equation 6.

$$\left(\frac{0.11 \text{ g HC}_2\text{H}_3\text{O}_2}{1 \text{ mL vinegar}}\right)\left(\frac{1 \text{ mL vinegar}}{1.02 \text{ g vinegar}}\right)(100\%)$$

$$= 11 \text{ mass percent acetic acid in commercial-grade vinegar} \qquad \text{(Eq. 6)}$$

In this experiment, you will determine the mass and density of a known volume of household vinegar. Then you will determine the volume of that vinegar required to completely react a known mass of baking soda. From these data, you will calculate the mass percent acetic acid in the household vinegar. You will also calculate the percent error in the labeled percent acetic acid, compared to your experimentally determined mass percent acetic acid.

PROCEDURE

Preview

- Record brand, type, and labeled percent acetic acid of the vinegar being analyzed
- Determine mass of 25.0 mL vinegar
- Determine the masses of several baking soda samples, to the nearest 0.01 g
- Add vinegar to baking soda solutions until bubbling stops; record vinegar volume used
- Dispose of materials safely

CAUTION

Wear departmentally approved safety goggles while doing this experiment.

1. On your Data Sheet, record the following data about the vinegar you are using: brand name, type (either distilled white or cider), and the percent acetic acid, based on the label information.

2. Obtain a clean, dry 7-oz plastic cup. Using a marker or wax pencil, label the cup "vinegar". Rinse the cup several times with a few milliliters of vinegar from the stock bottle, enough to cover the bottom of the cup for each rinse. Pour the rinses into the drain, diluting with a large amount of running water. After rinsing the cup, fill it three-quarters full with vinegar.

3. Rinse a clean, dry 50-mL graduated cylinder with three 5-mL portions of the vinegar from the cup. Then pour 25.0 mL of vinegar from the cup into the cylinder.

4. Obtain five additional clean, dry 7-oz plastic cups.

5. Tare one plastic cup on a balance. Pour the 25.0 mL of vinegar from the graduated cylinder into the cup. Allow sufficient time for the cylinder to drain completely into the cup. Using the same balance, measure the mass of the 25.0 mL of vinegar in the cup. Record this mass to the nearest 0.01 g on your Data Sheet.

6. On your Data Sheet, record the brand and the chemical formula of the baking soda you are using, based on the label information.

7. Label one of the four empty plastic cups "A". Tare the cup on a balance. Using a spatula, place 1.00–1.20 g of baking soda into this cup, weigh, and record the mass on your Data Sheet, to the nearest 0.01 g.

8. Using a clean 10-mL graduated cylinder, measure 5–10 mL of distilled or deionized water. Pour the water into cup A. Use a clean glass stirring rod to stir the mixture until all the baking soda has dissolved.

NOTE: In Steps 9–11, the solution will foam as CO_2 bubbles evolve. **Gentle swirling** will help release the bubbles.

---

9. Pour about 50 mL of vinegar from "vinegar" cup into the 50-mL graduated cylinder. On your Data Sheet, record this initial vinegar volume to the nearest milliliter. Add about 5 mL of vinegar from the cylinder to cup A, which contains the dissolved baking soda. *Swirl gently* to release the bubbles.

10. Continue to add vinegar from the graduated cylinder to cup A, a few milliliters at a time. Be careful not to add too much vinegar at once; if you do, the solution will foam out of the cup. Also, while gently swirling the cup, wait for all bubbles to disperse before adding the next portion of vinegar. When the rate of bubbling starts to diminish with each addition of vinegar, reduce the vinegar portions to 1 mL each. After each addition, gently swirl the cup until all bubbling ceases.

11. On your Data Sheet, record this final volume of vinegar left in the graduated cylinder (to the nearest milliliter) when the addition of 1 mL of vinegar no longer produces bubbling.

12. Label the three remaining cups "B", "C", and "D". Working with one cup at a time, tare the cup, place the mass of baking soda listed in Table 2 into the cup, and weigh. Record each baking soda mass to the nearest 0.01 g on your Data Sheet.

13. Add about 5–10 mL of distilled water to cups B–D, and stir to dissolve the baking soda.

14. Repeat Steps 9–11 for cups B–D. Record all volumes to the nearest milliliter on your Data Sheet.

Table 2 *Mass of baking soda to be placed into each labeled cup*

cup	mass, baking soda, g
B	1.4–1.6
C	1.9–2.1
D	2.4–2.6

15. Pour the contents of all cups into the drain, diluting with a large amount of running water. Rinse the cups with tap water. Then place all cups in the location specified by your laboratory instructor.

16. Wash your graduated cylinders with detergent solution, rinse with tap water, and invert to dry.

CAUTION

Wash your hands thoroughly with soap or detergent before leaving the laboratory.

CALCULATIONS

Do the following calculations for each determination, and record the results on your Data Sheet.

1. Using Equation 5, calculate the density of your 25.0-mL household vinegar sample.

2. Calculate the individual volumes (in milliliters) of vinegar added to cups *A–D*.

3. Prepare a graph that you can use to find the grams of baking soda required to react completely with 1.0 mL of your vinegar. To do so, use the graph paper provided to plot milliliters of vinegar used, on the *x*-axis, versus the corresponding grams of baking soda used, on the *y*-axis. Draw the best straight line passing through the origin and your four data points.

   Determine the slope of the straight line by choosing two points on the line that are not data points and dividing the difference in their *y* values by the difference in their *x* values. Note that the units associated with this slope are grams of $NaHCO_3$ per milliliter of vinegar. Hence, the slope of the line equals the grams of baking soda required to completely react 1 mL of your vinegar.

   Alternately, your laboratory instructor may ask you to use a computer spreadsheet program to perform regression analysis on your experimental data, plot the data, and calculate the slope of the best straight line.

4. Substituting $NaHCO_3$ for $KHCO_3$ in Equation 4, convert grams of $NaHCO_3$ per milliliter of vinegar to the equivalent numbers of grams of $HC_2H_3O_2$ per milliliter of vinegar, using the molar mass of $NaHCO_3$ (84.0 g/mol).

5. Using Equation 6, determine the mass percent $HC_2H_3O_2$ in your vinegar sample.

6. Calculate the percent error in the mass percent acetic acid listed on the vinegar label, as compared to your experimentally determined mass percent acetic acid.

Name   Section   Date

Post-Laboratory Questions

(Use the spaces provided for the answers and additional paper if necessary.)

1. One possible source of error in this experiment is to add more than 1 mL of vinegar before realizing that the solution is no longer bubbling. Suppose that, for each of your determinations, you consistently add 2 mL vinegar more than was required to completely react the baking soda in solution. Based on this assumption:

   (a) Recalculate your experimental data to correct it.

   (b) Using your corrected data prepare a graph on the next page, and determine the mass of acetic acid per milliliter of vinegar.

   (c) Determine the mass percent acetic acid in the vinegar.

2. As described in the Background Information, the stoichiometry of Equation 1 relates moles of $NaHCO_3$ to moles of $HC_2H_3O_2$ required for complete reaction of both reactants. It also relates moles of $NaHCO_3$ to moles of CO_2 gas produced.

   (a) Calculate the mass (in grams) of CO_2 gas produced by the reaction in cup B of your experiment.

   (b) One mole of CO_2 gas has a volume of about 22 L under standard conditions. Calculate the volume (in milliliters) of CO_2 gas produced by the reaction in cup B.

3. In a reaction similar to the one between baking soda and vinegar, limestone ($CaCO_3$) reacts with hydrochloric acid (HCl) solution to produce water and CO_2 gas. Write the balanced chemical equation for this reaction.

_____   _____   _____
Name   *Section*   *Date*

Data Sheet

vinegar: brand _____

                type _____

                percent acetic acid on label, % _____

                mass of 25 mL of vinegar, g _____

baking soda: brand _____

                   formula _____

cup	mass of baking soda, g	initial volume of vinegar, mL	final volume of vinegar, mL	volume of vinegar added to cup, mL
A	_____	_____	_____	_____
B	_____	_____	_____	_____
C	_____	_____	_____	_____
D	_____	_____	_____	_____

vinegar density, g/mL _____

slope of best straight line drawn using data points on your graph, g $NaHCO_3$/mL vinegar _____

grams of $HC_2H_3O_2$ per milliliter of vinegar, g/mL _____

mass percent $HC_2H_3O_2$ in vinegar, % _____

percent error, % _____

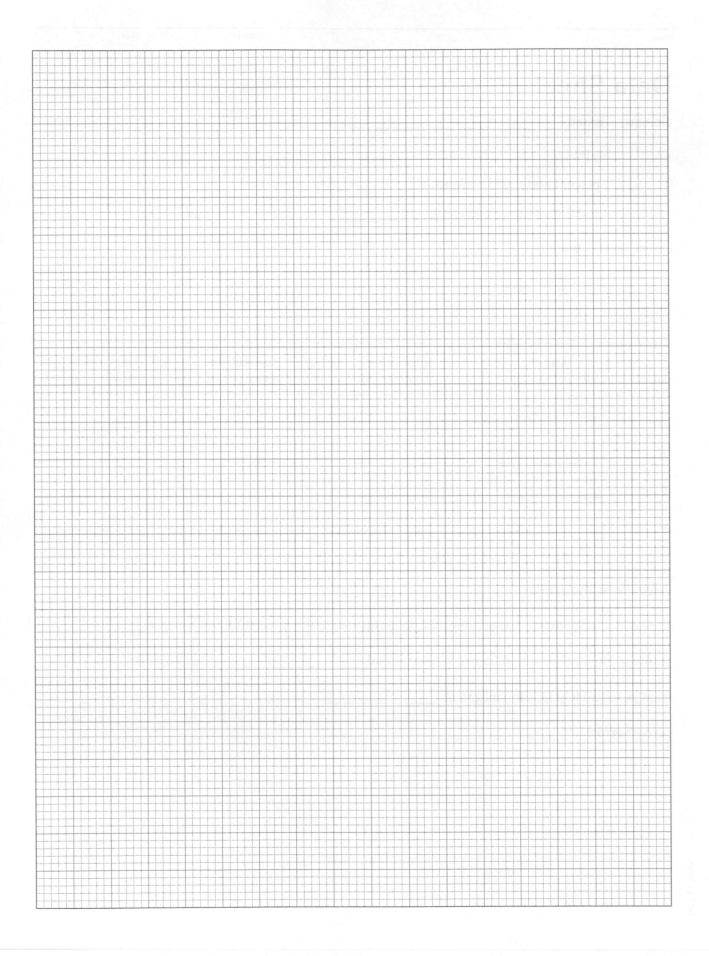

Name   Section   Date

Pre-Laboratory Assignment

1. Identify the chemicals present in the following substances:

(a) baking soda

(b) vinegar

2. The reaction of ammonium bicarbonate, NH_4HCO_3, with acetic acid, $HC_2H_3O_2$, in vinegar can be described by the following chemical equation.

$$NH_4HCO_3(s) + HC_2H_3O_2(aq) \rightarrow NH_4^+(aq) + C_2H_3O_2^-(aq) + H_2O\ (l) + CO_2(g)$$

An experiment was performed to determine the volume of vinegar required to completely react a known mass of NH_4HCO_3. The experimental data were:

NH_4HCO_3, g	vinegar, mL
0.62	10
0.85	14
1.14	19
1.31	23

(a) Using the above data and the graph paper supplied, plot the mass of NH_4HCO_3 on the *y*-axis versus the corresponding volume of vinegar on the *x*-axis. Draw the best straight line that passes through the data points and the origin.

(b) Determine the slope of this line, including the proper units. Your laboratory instructor may tell you to use a computer spreadsheet program or scientific calculator to produce the graph and determine the slope of the best straight line, using regression analysis.

(c) Use the calculated slope, the molar masses of NH_4HCO_3 and $HC_2H_3O_2$, and the stoichiometry of the reaction equation to determine the grams of $HC_2H_3O_2$ present per milliliter of the vinegar used in this experiment.

(d) Assuming that the density of the vinegar used in the experiment was approximately 1.0 g/mL, determine the mass percent $HC_2H_3O_2$ in the vinegar.